"*Warding Off Evildoers* by Joan Tr
anyone serious about understand
origins of evil. This book is packed full of interesting details and
studies and provides some great insight into the architecture of evil.
Joan has a knack for writing in a very engaging and conversational
tone, and the end result is a scholarly book that reads almost like a
novel. Do yourself a favor and read this important book.
You will be glad that you did."

—KEVIN BEAVER, PhD, a professor of criminology
at Florida State University in Tallahassee

———

"Ms. Treichel's book is well written, fascinating, and easy to read.
It is also very well researched, and she has summarized a significant
number of relevant findings. Numerous powerful examples are
presented of individuals who have caused great harm to others,
and their stories (though often gruesome) beg for understanding
from a mental health perspective."

—FRED Berlin, MD, PhD, an associate professor
of psychiatry at Johns Hopkins University School of Medicine
in Baltimore, Maryland

———

"This book by Joan Arehart-Treichel regarding evildoers addresses
a complex and gruesome topic. Through the presentation of
numerous case vignettes, Ms. Arehart-Treichel outlines many
types of evil behavior, such as serial murder, sexual sadism, rape,
pedophilia, arson, bullying, stalking, and other bad acts. When

it comes to explaining what drives evil actors, she relies on the research and writings of many experts in this field of study. Thus, she explains and illustrates various motivations, such as envy, greed, having fun, hatred, revenge, sexual pleasure, childhood maltreatment, and genetics. This is a difficult topic, as there are no easy answers for the dark side of human nature. It seems likely, though, that understanding the scope of the activities of evildoers will reduce the harm they inflict on the good doers in our communities."

—WILLIAM BERNET, MD, a professor of psychiatry emeritus at Vanderbilt University in Nashville, Tennessee

―――――

"*Warding Off Evildoers* is clearly a catchy subject. From a scientific point of view, the construction of a scale of 'evil' from the public's perspective would be of great interest as public perception influences how crimes are perceived by prosecutors. Such a scale might also look at how 'evil' members of the public view sexual abuse versus assault versus larceny versus child molestation versus rape [and so on]. A description of such attitudes would be of great interest to our correctional system, I think."

—RICHARD KRUEGER, MD, a clinical professor of psychiatry at Columbia University College of Physicians and Surgeons in New York City

―――――

"This proceeds as a pacey, page-turning narrative for a book about science, [and] the author manages to avoid almost completely a pointless debate about 'nature versus nurture.' Instead, she shows persuasively that both genes and environment have important roles [in the making of evildoers]."

—PETER MCGUFFIN, MD, an emeritus professor of psychiatric genetics at the Institute of Psychiatry, King's College, London, England

––––––

"Joan Treichel's well organized, user-friendly, and powerful book about evil is packed with important information. It is also rare since the concept of evil is not discussed often, meaningfully, or comprehensively by scholars and various media. The author provides succinct definitions of evil and summarizes countless studies and media reports of various antisocial behaviors -- from bullying and pathological lying to sexual abuse of children, serial-killing, and violent crime. Her chapters on what is associated with evil also attend to a wide range of areas—from birth injury to brain structure to parental mental health and to conduct disorder in children. Ultimately, she emphasizes that an interaction of influencers, not just one, contributes to evil—purposefully and intentionally causing suffering. This book is a must-read for every professional involved in the fields of mental health, medicine, law, social work, and K-12 education."

—JEAN PETERSON, PhD, a professor emerita at Purdue University in West Lafayette, Indiana

WARDING

OFF

EVILDOERS

ARMINLEAR

Library of Congress Control Number: 2022932532

ISBN (paperback):978-1-956450-25-5
      (eBook): 978-1-956450-26-2

Armin Lear Press Inc
215 W Riverside Drive, #4362
Estes Park, CO 80517

WARDING

OFF

EVILDOERS

JOAN AREHART-TREICHEL

ARMINLEAR

For Fritz:
"If you could do it over,
would you still become
a Nazi?"

ACKNOWLEDGMENTS

This work is based on research conducted by several hundred scientists exploring various aspects of evildoing. Many are still passionately at it. I am indebted to each of them for their hard efforts.

I am particularly grateful to those scientists who took the time to critique some or all of my manuscript since the subject is complex and controversial. They include: Kevin Beaver, PhD, a professor of criminology at Florida State University in Tallahassee, Florida and a researcher into the biosocial underpinnings of antisocial behaviors; Fred Berlin, MD, PhD, an associate professor of psychiatry at Johns Hopkins University School of Medicine in Baltimore, Maryland and an expert on sexual offending and treatment; William Bernet, MD, a professor of psychiatry emeritus at Vanderbilt University School of Medicine in Nashville, Tennessee, as well as a forensic psychiatrist who has testified in numerous states and who has written about such provocative subjects as satanic ritual abuse; Richard Krueger, MD, a clinical professor of psychiatry at Columbia University College of Physicians and Surgeons in New York City and medical director of the Sexual Behavior Clinic at New York State Psychiatric Institute there; Peter McGuffin, MD, an emeritus professor of psychiatric genetics at the Institute of Psychiatry, King's College, London,

England; and Jean Peterson, PhD, a professor emerita at Purdue University in West Lafayette, Indiana, as well as an expert on gifted children and bullying.

My deep appreciation goes to my amazing literary agent-editor Maryann Karinch, who believed in my book from the start, honed it, brought it to the light of day, and is now spurring its distribution not only in the United States, but throughout the world.

My two daughters, too, gave me their unfailing support and provided me with valuable suggestions during the many months while I was putting the book together. They are Tamara Treichel, PhD, of Beijing, China (an author in her own right with a book soon to be published by China Intercontinental Press) and Heidi Treichel of Berlin, Germany (a logistics expert who arranged the transport of works of fine art first out of New York City, then subsequently out of Berlin, to faraway destinations).

Finally, my husband Horst Treichel would certainly have championed me during my *Evildoers* undertaking had he still been alive to do so. He was not only my beloved husband of 42 years, but also my best friend and greatest confident, especially during those many months when I was working on other books.

PREFACE

I have long been terrified of, yet also fascinated by, evil.

It may have started with the Halloween bonfires at the end of our street when I was little. They seemed to conjure up sinister spirits harking back to Celtic times. Or it may have commenced with my obsessive "dirty" thoughts, which I feared would damn me to hell. In any event, it was cemented by an experience that I had at age nine. I came across two neighborhood boys while they were pulling the legs off a grasshopper one by one. Do grasshoppers feel pain? The boys hoped so.

But my front-row seat on evil, so to speak, only came in 2000 when I became a senior staff writer for *Psychiatric News,* which is published by the American Psychiatric Association for psychiatrists around the United States. My responsibilities included writing about advances in various fields of psychiatry. One of these was "forensic psychiatry," that is, psychiatry of the criminal mind.

As I covered this domain over the years, I attended lectures, read research papers, and interviewed psychiatrists and some other professionals who were expert on the subject. I also came face to face with a few individuals who had committed chilling deeds. For instance, I chatted with a young woman in the forensic wing of a mental hospital who had killed her parents. I visited San Quentin State Prison in California and looked a death-row prisoner in the eye as he was escorted past me by two guards. I wrote articles about my findings for *Psychiatric News,* but also stowed material for an eventual book on the subject. Now is the time, I believe, to share my findings with the public.

There are already some good books about evildoers on the market, notably *The Evil That Men Do,* by Federal Bureau of Investigation (FBI) sex predator profiler Roy Hazelwood and true crime writer Stephen Michaud, and published by St. Martin's Press in 1998; *Bad Men Do What Good Men Dream,* by forensic psychiatrist Robert I. Simon, MD, and published by American Psychiatric Publishing in 2008; and *The Anatomy of Evil,* by forensic psychiatrist Michael Stone, MD, and published by Prometheus Books in 2009. All three books, essentially, are based on the authors' professional knowledge, observations, and analyses.

In his book, for example, Simon examines the lives of some rapists, stalkers, murderers, and other people who have committed dastardly deeds in order to illuminate if possible why they did what they did. Stone does something similar, but he also categorizes such people according to the extent of their depravity.

In contrast, *Warding Off Evildoers* taps not only the knowledge, observations, and analyses of forensic experts, but also scientific study findings to see what they can tell us about who evildoers are, how they got that way, and most crucially, how we can protect ourselves and our loved ones from them. I also make the argument, as does Simon in his book, that we all have evil impulses in us and offer suggestions, based on forensic experts' observations and analyses, as well as on forensic study findings, as to how we can keep from becoming evildoers ourselves or turning our children into one.

My German friend Ingrid is still baffled why her father Fritz became an impassioned Nazi and was willing to die for Hitler.

—JOAN AREHART-TREICHEL
Sherwood Forest, Maryland, USA
June 2022

CONTENTS

ONE
DEFINING EVILDOERS

It was one of the last sessions of the American Psychiatric Association's 2001 annual meeting in New Orleans. The room was packed with psychiatrists and members of the press, including myself. All of us had come to hear about a subject that fascinates—and terrifies—most of us. The subject was evil.

One of the speakers was an older man with graying hair; a high forehead; narrow-set, piercing brown eyes; a rather prominent nose, and a serious demeanor. Another was a tall, dark, and handsome younger man with a cavalier manner. The former was Michael Stone, MD, the latter Michael Welner, MD. Both were New York City forensic psychiatrists.

Stone, we in the audience would soon learn, had what he described as a "morbid hobby"—collecting and analyzing information about the lives of people who had done "breathtakingly awful" things. In addition to reading over 400 biographies of such individuals, he had interviewed serial killers in prison to learn what made them tick. He had now toted the biographies of some 100 serial killers to the symposium in his laptop computer and was ready to regale us with some chilling details about them.

Welner, we would soon learn, also had a passion—creating a new scientific instrument called the Depravity Scale that would standardize the definition of evil behavior.

But first things first. The title of the symposium was "How Psychiatry Defines Evil." And Welner, with some panache, set about honing a definition.

"How do you define depravity?" Welner asked the audience.

"Beyond what we consider acceptable," one doctor ventured.

"Can you give me an example?" Welner asked.

"I don't know," the doctor replied. "I'm from the Netherlands!" (Chuckles from the audience)

"Evil is essentially subjecting others to long, horrible pain," Stone proposed. "I think most of us would agree."

"I do not!" a psychiatrist in the audience retorted.

"People who do evil do not feel that it's evil," another doctor in the audience opined. "Only their victims believe that."

"I'm not so sure I agree," Welner commented.

Still another audience member argued that we should all avoid using the word "evil" and instead call it "depravity," "wantonness," or "inhumanity." He was John L. Young, MD, a forensic psychiatrist from New Haven, Connecticut and a Catholic priest. "I feel goose bumps when people talk about evil," he confessed.

I later asked Young why he had made that statement. "I have great respect for the power of evil," he replied, "whether you want to personify it as Lucifer, Satan, the Devil, or even not at all. I think that defining evil is outside our competence, professionally or spiritually."

In short, there was no consensus on what evil is. But as Stone pointed out at one point during the discussion, "We tend to reserve the term 'evil' for the intentional hurt of others."

That, in my opinion, is a compelling definition, and the definition I will use in my book: *Evildoers are individuals who intentionally hurt others.*

TWO
WHAT ARE THEIR MOTIVES?

Back during the 1960s and 1970s, O.J. Simpson was a gorgeous hunk of a professional football player. He was also so spectacular at his game that he was induced into the Pro Football Hall of Fame in 1985.

On a foggy June night in 1994, though, his estranged wife, Nicole Brown Simpson, and her friend Ron Goldman, were found slashed to death outside of Nicole's Brentwood, California condo. Simpson was a prime suspect. Jealousy could have driven him to kill Nicole and her lover, the police reasoned. He likewise had the brawn to easily carry out such a slaughter. And he led the police on a freeway chase rather than turn himself in for questioning.

Ultimately the police caught him. He was charged with the two murders and put on trial. His 13-month trial was televised and became the most widely watched criminal trial in history. Millions of people, including myself, were mesmerized by it. Could Simpson's "Dream Team" of pricey lawyers get him off? I can still recall the moment when the jury foreman announced a verdict of "not guilty." Simpson looked stunned; then a small smile lit up his face.

However, Simpson's charmed life didn't last. A civil jury later found him liable for both deaths and ordered him to cough up some $33 million in damages. He had to sell his posh mansion among other valuables. In 2007, he was arrested in Los Vegas and charged with armed robbery and kidnapping. In 2008, he was convicted and sentenced to 33 years of imprisonment with a minimum of nine years without the possibility of parole. He served his sentence in a Nevada prison; was granted parole on July 20, 2017; and was released from prison on October 1, 2017.

So did Simpson murder his wife and her lover? And if so, did jealousy prompt him to do it? Only O.J. knows, and he isn't talking.

Jealousy, in any event, is a common reason why men kill their wives, evildoer expert Michael Stone, MD, (introduced in the previous chapter) tells us. He came to this conclusion after analyzing the forensic records of 75 wife murderers. He also found that these wife slayers tended to be highly narcissistic and to have carried out the murders just as their spouses were about to leave them. Makes sense, no?

Jealousy also appears to alchemize some individuals into stalkers, Harald Dressing, MD, of the Central Institute of Mental Health in Mannheim, Germany, and coworkers reported in the August 2005 *British Journal of Psychiatry.*

Jealousy, however, is only one of many reasons why people engage in detestable behaviors, researchers, experts on the subject, and true-life dramas tell us. Here are more.

A BID FOR ATTENTION

A team of Australian, British, and American researchers set out to learn why people sometimes attempt to harass or attack the British Royal Family. They found 23 individuals who had been arrested for such attempts and studied their forensic records. Most of the individuals had engaged in such behavior to draw attention to themselves or to their particular grievances, the researchers found. The findings were published in the spring 2008 *Journal the American Academy of Psychiatry and the Law.*

His name was Robert Steinhaueser. In 2002, he was a teen in the German city of Erfurt. He was a loner, lacked self-esteem, and created a world for himself from Heavy-Metal music, brutal computer games, and weapons.

One morning, he donned a black outfit, put on a mask, and stole into his high school with two weapons. He used them to kill 13 teachers, two students, and a policeman before killing himself.

The reason? "I want to be well known and famous," he had commented shortly before carrying out his slaughter.

A HUNGER FOR APPROVAL

In 1985, a boy named Lee Malvo was born on the Caribbean Island of Jamaica. His childhood was far from idyllic. His father was working off-island, and Malvo missed him terribly. His mother suspected his father of infidelity and took out her rage on Malvo, beating him with belts, brooms, and switches. He witnessed his first killing at age seven while walking to school. For a while, he lived with his mother in a shack with no plumbing or electricity on the Caribbean island of Antigua. Eventually she abandoned him there. He now had to fend for himself.

In 2000, however, when Malvo was 15 years old, it looked as if his fortunes might be turning. He met an American named John Allen Muhammad on Antigua. Muhammad appeared willing to play the father Malvo had never had. Before long, Malvo was calling him "Dad." When Muhammad returned to the United States, he even brought Malvo along with him.

Yet once he arrived there, Malvo quickly learned that it hadn't been a free ride: Muhammad expected him to be capable of taking a human life. Thus, two days before he turned age 17, he shot a woman in the face in Tacoma, Washington to demonstrate that he had the guts to do it. And once he and Muhammad relocated to the Washington, DC area, he helped Muhammad randomly kill 17 more people for the sport of it. Actually, the two terrorized people in the area for more than three weeks. I can still remember how so many Washingtonians, including my husband and myself, were afraid to stop at gas stations because Muhammad and Malvo targeted many of their victims when they got out of their cars to tank up.

Muhammad, who earned the moniker "the Washington sniper" for this deadly killing spree, was eventually captured, tried, found guilty, and sentenced to death. He was executed in a Virginia death chamber in 2009. Malvo was also captured, tried, found guilty, and sentenced to life in prison. Why had he assisted Muhammad in such truculent acts? "I was desperate to fill a void in my life, and I was ready to give my life for him," he confessed to Vermont psychiatrist Diane Schetky, MD. Schetky served as an expert witness for the defense at his trial.

A LUST FOR POWER

Rapists tend to be driven by a lust for power, various forensic experts have found. A lust for power also appears to have played a key role in the blood sports and deadly games performed in ancient Rome, historian, and researcher Donald G. Kyle reports. "Clearly spectacles were political devices used by leaders to gain support and to appease the masses under autocratic regimes," he wrote in the January/February 2000 issue of *Odyssey*. Moreover, while some Romans attended these performances in order to see and be seen, to court, to gamble, to meet the emperor, or to be thrilled by the sight of foreigners and exotic animals, others clearly did so because they "were drawn by the allure of violence and power," Kyle notes.

He seemed to be such a "jolly good" man, Harold Shipman—a physician practicing near Manchester, a city in northern England. He was quiet, bespectacled, and sported a white beard. He had a wife and four children, was respected by his community. Yet he was engaging in a diabolical activity that no one, in their wildest imagination, would ever have imagined.

When he made house calls on middle-aged or older women who lived alone, he injected them with a lethal substance. He managed to persuade their relatives that they had died from natural causes, and that an autopsy wasn't needed. Shipman was finally apprehended, convicted of murdering 15 of his patients by lethal injection, and sentenced to 15 consecutive life terms. Actually he had murdered 215, possibly even 260 patients, over a period of 23 years, an official inquiry eventually divulged. Apparently, Shipman had never taken the Hippocratic oath—to do his patients no harm!

These revelations shocked people throughout Britain and made headlines for months. Shipman's crimes were "wicked, wicked," his trial judge declared. But what had prompted him to engage in them? A desire to play God, many believed.

ENVY

Although it's been decades since I attended college, I can still feel the shock and dismay I felt when I discovered that my chemistry textbook was missing right before a chemistry exam. *How am I going to study for the exam and keep up my grade-point average?* I agonized. I asked around on my dorm floor, but nobody admitted to having seen my chemistry textbook. I went up to the dorm floor above mine and asked around again. To my great relief, I spotted the textbook in one of the dorm rooms; it was lying open on the desk of a student named "Gail." Gail was in the room at the time. "What is my textbook doing on your desk?" I demanded.

"I just wanted to check something," she mumbled. She slapped the book shut and handed it over to me.

Only later did I learn that hiding textbooks was a "time-honored" habit that mediocre students engage in to sabotage the success of more academically ambitious students. So envy, it seemed, was Gail's incentive for hiding my textbook. But what hurt most was that I had liked her and had thought we were on the way to becoming friends.

FUN

Why are some youngsters cruel to animals? Christopher Hensley, PhD, an associate professor of criminal justice at the University of Tennessee in Chattanooga, and Suzanne Tallichet, PhD, a professor of sociology at Morehead (Kentucky) State University, came up with a clever ploy to answer this question—by interviewing prison inmates. After all, many criminals launch their careers by torturing animals.

Hensley and Tallichet found 261 inmates in either a medium-security or a maximum-security prison who were willing to talk with them about this subject. Of those inmates who admitted to having tortured animals, they gave one of two different reasons why. They were angry and took their anger out on animals. Or they found it fun to engage in such a sport. And if they did it for kicks, that was an especially potent predictor that they were on their way to a life of violent crime, the researchers determined. The results appeared in the April 2008 *International Journal of Offender Therapy and Comparative Criminology*.

GREED

Bernard Madoff was a native New Yorker who rose from modest beginnings to become a silver-haired, distinguished-looking, legendary Wall Street financier. Yet in the fall of 2008, when the world economy nosedived, Madoff knew that his high-flying lifestyle, which included a posh apartment in Manhattan; an ocean-front house in Montauk, Long Island; a home in Palm Beach, Florida; and a house in France, was crashing as well.

On December 10, he confessed to his two sons that he had been living a big lie—running a Ponzi scheme, whereby he promised investors a consistently high rate of return, yet used money from new investors to pay off older investors and himself. The sons alerted the authorities. On December 11, Federal Bureau of Investigation (FBI) agents arrived to arrest Madoff on fraud charges. In March 2009, Madoff confessed to his crimes, and in June 2009, a judge sentenced him to 150 years in prison, declaring that he had committed crimes that were "extraordinarily evil."

Indeed, Madoff had cheated not only millionaires, private foundations, a Nobel Prize laureate, and hundreds of small investors of a whopping $65 billion—making it one of the largest frauds in Wall Street history—but had also spurred one of his sons to commit suicide on the second anniversary of his father's arrest. And in February 2022, Bernie Madoff's sister, Sondra Wiener, and her husband were found dead in their Florida home in an apparent murder-suicide.

HATRED

On a Sunday morning in 2012, a 40-year-old man named Wade Page walked into a Sikh temple in Oak Creek, Wisconsin right before services were to begin. He gunned down six people before killing himself. His motive was undoubtedly hate since he was a well-known white supremacist and played in a band called Definite Hate.

MERCY

How could anyone possibly kill his or her own child? Yet it happens. So, an expert on filicide —Phillip Resnick, MD, a professor of psychiatry at Case Western University in Cleveland—examined the reasons why people engage in such deplorable acts. One is to spare a child from real or imagined suffering. Another is to include a child in one's own suicide attempt so that it won't be left behind, Resnick found.

ROMANCE

According to stalking expert Harald Dressing (cited above), stalkers aren't always driven by jealousy or another malignant motive. Sometimes they are motivated by something much more positive, such as a desire for a loving relationship or a yearning to resume one.

SEXUAL PLEASURE

In her book *Predators,* Dr. Anna Salter writes about a man who repeatedly raped his stepson. He told Salter that he was so aroused sexually from inflicting pain that he would do "anything to justify my actions."

Sexual gratification also plays a key role in most serial killings, Paul Appelbaum, MD, a Columbia University forensic psychiatrist, reported in an editorial published in the October 15, 2002 *Washington Post*. Serial killers "derive a sexual-like excitement from their moments of deadly intimacy with their victims," Appelbaum noted.

Sexual turn-ons may also power rituals that serial sex killers often engage in. So suggested Louis Schlesinger, PhD, a professor of psychology at the John Jay College of Criminal Justice in New York City, and colleagues in the April-May 2000 issue of the *Journal of the American Academy of Psychiatry and the Law*.

Schlesinger and his team examined the records of 38 serial sex killers and found that 97 percent had engaged in rituals with at least two of their victims. Such rituals consisted of behaviors that exceeded those necessary to cause death, for example, torturing the victim beforehand, having sex with the corpse after death, dismembering the corpse, or taking mementos from the corpse. Remember the 1991 movie thriller *The Silence of the Lambs?* In this thriller, a serial sex killer didn't take a memento from his victims, but rather left a memento with them: a moth in their mouths.

REVENGE WINS THE PRIZE

Yet, of the vast number of the reasons why people engage in pernicious behaviors, a lust to "get even" may well be the most prevalent incentive. Think about it: Nothing upsets people more than being ill-treated, having their "good name" tarnished, or being cheated out of what they consider rightfully theirs. Not just forensic research and forensic experts, but true stories tend to bolster this position..

April 20, 1999 was an infamous day in Columbine, Colorado. Two students at Columbine High School, Eric Harris and Dillon Kliebold, taunted and then killed 13 fellow students before committing suicide in the school library. The reason? They apparently viewed themselves as avengers for nerds in the school, such as themselves, who had been bullied by jocks.

Some years ago, a couple named Dr. Zakaria and Marianne Oweiss lived in the posh Washington, DC suburb of Potomac, Maryland. I knew the couple a bit since their older son was in the same class as my younger daughter in the Washington, DC German School, which is located in Potomac. Dr. Oweiss was originally from Egypt, his wife originally from Germany. Marianne flew to Zakaria's hometown in Egypt and engaged in an extramarital affair. When she returned, he bludgeoned her to death, presumably to redeem his family's honor.

Honor killings, where a wife is killed by her spouse or family for her presumably immoral behavior, occur in many Islamic countries, Amin Muhammad Gadit, MD, a Pakistani psychiatrist now living in Canada, told me during an interview. Such slayings are carried out because of a cultural mindset, not because they are legally sanctioned in Muslim countries. "There have [also] been several such cases in Canada," Gadit told me. "So the [Canadian] Department of Justice wants me to give them a position paper on the international magnitude of honor killings and their relevance to Canada."

On some occasions, though, women act to defend their own honor. On the night of June 23, 1993, a Virginia woman named Lorena Bobbitt became fed up with her husband's alleged physical and sexual abuse and decided to get even. She took a kitchen knife, cut off his penis while he was sleeping, then threw the penis out of her car window onto Highway 66.

Later, when I heard about this audacious act, I thought, *Wow! What an ingenious way to take revenge.*

Her husband, however, may have ultimately triumphed: Police found the penis, and doctors re-attached it surgically to his body.

THREE
ARE SOME EVILDOERS MORE DEPRAVED THAN OTHERS?

"Evil? The word conjures up creepy organ music," Joseph Merlino, MD, a New York City psychiatrist, once commented. "But actually evil is present in the small, petty cruelties of everyday life."

Yet does that mean that a teen who vandalizes a car is as depraved as a tyrannical, mildly abusing husband? And is the latter as nefarious as a woman who forced feces into her stepdaughter's mouth if the stepdaughter did not work fast enough? And how about the man who blew up his son's puppy with a bomb while the son was present?

There are obviously no easy ways to determine whether this or that evildoer is more wanton than another since it concerns individual moral judgment. Nonetheless, evildoer experts—notably forensic psychiatrists Michael Stone, MD, and Michael Welner, MD, who were introduced in the first chapter—can offer us some tentative answers.

In 1987, Stone was asked to serve as an expert witness in a murder case. It involved Jeffrey McDonald, who was charged with killing his pregnant wife and two little daughters. The case stimulated Stone's interest in murderers.

He started reading biographies of infamous murderers—those found in the true-crime section of bookstores—because these books generally give a great amount of personal detail about each murderer. As of 2003, he had read 447 such biographies, and as of 2009, some 600. And by 2009, he had also read some 500 magazine or newspaper articles about notorious murderers and had interviewed a number of them in prison. Altogether he had acquired an extensive database of some 1,200 murderers, 145 of whom were serial sex killers.

This ever-growing database in turn allowed Stone to answer some questions of passionate interest to him: What types of people murder, what factors prompt them to do this or that, and how depraved are certain ones compared to others?

In his efforts to build a "Gradations-of-Evil Scale" for the murderers in his database, Stone first rated them as "not depraved," "possibly depraved," or "for sure depraved." For instance, as he told me during an interview, "Killing a pregnant wife and two kids is pretty bad, but it was done with dispatch, you might say, and it was relatively painless. I felt that as bad as it was, it did not reach the level of Ian Brady and his girlfriend-accomplice Myra Hindley." Back during the 1960s, Brady had lured children into a cottage on the English moor. He recorded their screams while he strangled them. He then played the tapes back later for himself and Myra as a sort of aphrodisiac.

After that, Stone fleshed out his Gradations-of-Evil Scale to include 22 categories. A common thread running through almost all of the categories was the element of intentionality. He placed murderers who committed homicide in self-defense at the bottom of the scale; murderers demonstrating psychopathic traits, such as narcissism, lack of empathy, lying, and conning, further up the scale (more about psychopathy in the next chapter); and psychopathic murderers who enjoyed torturing their victims at the very top.

WELNER TOOK ANOTHER TACK

Welner's interest in determining which evildoers are more pernicious than others started, as it had for Stone, while serving as an expert witness in criminal cases. However, Welner took a totally different route than Stone did to find the answers.

During his work for both the prosecution and defense, Welner noted that many states had laws stating that if a murder is considered "heinous," "atrocious," or "cruel," it heightens culpability and may make them eligible for the death penalty. Yet there was no consensus regarding the meaning of such words. For instance, in some instances, offenses were found to be cruel because of the fear and emotional stress they placed on victims. In other instances, offenses were found to be cruel if the victim was conscious for only a few seconds.

As a result, defendants were at the mercy of each court's interpretation, so that if a defendant's act was judged "heinous," "atrocious," or "cruel" in one jurisdiction, it might not be in another. Welner believed that a consensus about what constituted extremely vile behavior was desperately needed to make the American criminal justice system more equitable, particularly in those cases where the death penalty was an option.

But who should come up such a consensus? Theologians? Forensic psychiatrists? Probably the latter, Welner reasoned, since forensic psychiatrists are the ones who read entire criminal cases, evaluate the psychological state of defendants, and make judgment calls about their state of mind before, during, and after the crime committed. In other words, as Welner recalled, "I didn't think it would be a stretch for us forensic psychiatrists to define depravity as long as we were cautious."

And if forensic psychiatrists were truly the right professionals to define "heinous," ""atrocious," and "cruel," how should they go about it? Perhaps by creating a scientific instrument that reflected public consensus about the terms. Welner pondered. Such an instrument could then be used to help juries and judges decide whether this or that act was despicable or extremely so.

Ultimately Welner decided to undertake the development of such an instrument himself. He named it the "Depravity Scale."

The first phase of the research began in 1998. It involved a review of more than 100 higher- court decisions on capital cases (cases where the death penalty was an option) to find examples of where courts had found crimes to be extremely loathsome and why. Subsequently Welner and his colleagues reviewed the psychiatric literature to glean diagnostic correlates for sentences the courts had issued in such cases. They then used the information to flesh out a Depravity Scale model that contained 26 different items possibly reflecting depravity or extreme depravity. For instance, "intent to emotionally traumatize a victim," "intent to permanently disfigure a victim," "prolonging a victim's suffering," and "indifference or satisfaction after inflicting suffering on a victim" were four of the proposed items.

Subsequently, members of the public were invited to log onto the Depravity Scale Web site and to give their opinions as to whether any or all of these items truly represented depraved or extremely depraved behavior.

By 2002, some 2,500 individuals had provided their inputs. They included Americans, Canadians, and Europeans; males and females; whites and nonwhites; urban and rural residents; young, middle-aged, and older individuals.

Some subgroups tended to rate the items under consideration differently than did other subgroups. For instance, women tended to find the action items more depraved than men did. Rural residents were more likely to view certain actions as especially depraved than were urban residents. The 40-to-60-year-olds consistently singled out items as more depraved than did younger and older respondents. Minorities were more likely to flag "bearing false witness to cover yourself" as depraved than were whites.

But overall, there were no major differences in how respondents judged the items. New Yorkers, Californians, and Texans tended to respond the same as did people in Florida, North Carolina, and Tennessee. The same for Americans, Canadians, and Europeans. Over 90 percent of all respondents endorsed 16 out of 26 of the items as characterizing depravity or extreme depravity. Of the 16 items, nine had to do with intent, five with action, and two with attitude after the crime.

By 2007, some 25,000 individuals from over 50 countries had contributed to the scale. They tended to agree that three out of the 26 items especially mirrored extremely depraved behavior. One concerned intent and two actions. The intent item was "to purposefully cause emotional trauma." The action items were "to prolong suffering" and "to cause grotesque suffering."

As of 2016, the Depravity Scale (now called "the Depravity Standard") continued to be researched and refined. For instance, Welner and his colleagues planned to see whether the Standard could be used to accurately identify depravity in different types of crimes, for example murder, assault, a sex crime, or a nonviolent felony. And if so, they would then attempt to see how reliable (reproducible) the results were when repeated.

Thus, if we put Stone's Gradation-of-Evil Scale assessments as well as Welner's Depravity Standard results together, it looks as if the most malevolent of all evildoers are individuals who intentionally cause their victims agonizing pain and take pleasure in doing so.

In brief, they are sadists.

DEFINING A SADIST

But what is a sadist exactly? Evildoing and sadism are not the same thing, Stone explains. Evildoing is intentionally harming another person. Sadism is deriving pleasure from having inflicted such an injury. Take, for instance, a man who shot his daughter while he was on the phone with his ex-wife. The act was evil because he shot his daughter. But it was not sadistic in regards to the girl since she died immediately and experienced no pain. It *was* sadistic, however, in regards to the ex-wife since he derived pleasure from making her suffer. So, while not all evildoers are sadists, all sadists are evildoers—doubly wicked.

After having analyzed some 425 sadism cases, Stone concluded that men are more prone to sadism than are women, and that while sexual sadism appeared to be nonexistent among women, it is common among male serial killers. But Welner adds this caveat: "If we think it is only men who are sadists, we are kidding ourselves."

Youngsters, too, can act sadistically, child psychologist Peter Langman, PhD, reminds us in his book *Why Kids Kill – Inside the Minds of School Shooters*. One of the school shooters he discusses in his book was only 11 years old. Until then, the boy had behaved in an exemplary manner in the presence of his parents and teachers, yet was secretly torturing animals.

A major reason why people engage in sadism is to gain total control over their victim, Stone and Welner concur. For example, a man treated his mistress sadistically. When she tried to escape from him, he caught her, killed her, and packed her body in a trunk.

Research has also shown that a sadistic desire to control another person is often intermingled with sexual gratification, Welner notes. A chilling example of such interplay is provided by Ann Burgess, RN, a professor of nursing at the University of Pennsylvania who has had a lot of experience with rape victims.

A young man, whom we'll call Hank, was handsome and charming and before long gained the trust of a young woman. He called her his "pretty lady." One evening, she was driving him around in her convertible. He told her to make a particular turn. They ended up in a remote area, where he savagely raped, then killed her. When the police found her body, "there was a lot of blood everywhere," Burgess reports. "It looked as if she had been pounded against a car window." After Hank was apprehended, he simply shrugged it off as "rough sex." And after he had been found guilty and imprisoned, he recalled the experience with relish: "I loved watching her eyes widen with fear while I bit her."

Yet revenge, not a desire to control, drives some people to commit sadism, Stone informs us. Take this case from Japan: A man had a palm deformity and resented it to the point that he decided to seek retribution for it from society at large. He killed several children, chopped off their hands, and then mailed the hands to their parents.

Jealousy, too, sometimes powers sadism, Stone points out. So can a feeling of inferiority.

THE HALL OF INFAMY

Some sadists have become notorious throughout the years not just for the incredibly cruelty they have inflicted on others, but because of the positions of power they have held and because of the number of victims impacted.

For instance, a German named Hans Eisele served as a concentration camp physician under Hitler during World War II. Eisele performed stomach-resection operations on inmates in Dachau, the concentration camp near Munich, without giving them any anesthesia. Moreover, under Eisele's directive, inmates were sometimes housed in a tiny wooden box where they could not sit or lie down, but had to crouch, and received no food or water for three to seven days. At the end of that time, Eisele's underlings would take them out of the box, and if they were still alive, give them a pitcher of water to drink. Racked by thirst, they would guzzle the water, which caused their emaciated stomachs to protrude. Eisele's men would then throw them to the ground and stomp on them, rupturing their stomachs, and they would then die a slow and agonizing death. In short, "It was diabolical torture intended to maximize pain and humiliation," Stone declares.

Saddam Hussein ruled Iraq for 30 years, from 1979 to 2003. He was widely condemned for the brutality of his dictatorship. His invasions of Iran and Kuwait resulted in hundreds of thousands of deaths. On one occasion, he arrested a man who had written something critical of him, then boiled the man's hands in sulfuric acid until the man's hands dissolved before his very eyes. On another, he learned of a man who had made a careless remark in passing about his regime. He had the man arrested, fed into a meat grinder, and the man's remains returned to his family.

Other sadists may have inflicted as much pain on their victims as Eisele and Hussein did, yet are not widely known, either because they were not public figures or because the number of their victims was limited.

For instance, in 1977, an Austrian engineer named Josef Fritzl imprisoned his 18-year-old daughter Elizabeth in a bunker he had secretly constructed under the family house. He gave Elizabeth two choices: either incest or starvation. She choose the former. She ended up bearing him seven children, and she and the children only ended up seeing the light of day 24 years later, that is, in 2001 when Fritzl's diabolical crimes were finally discovered.

Or take the case of a Sacramento, California woman named Teresa Knorr. She tortured her children in various ways: She force-fed them, burned them with cigarettes, threw knives at them. As her two older daughters blossomed into attractive young women, she was racked with envy and decided to kill them both. In 1984, she starved one to death in a dark closet. In 1985, she poured gasoline over the other and burned her to death.

Still other sadists aren't known at all except by their victims. Indeed, sadists are much more common in everyday life than most of us realize, Stone warns us.

EVERYDAY SADISTS

They might be doctors, lawyers, or teachers; bosses or coworkers; fellow students; even family members.

"The sadistic traits seen in such serial killers as Jeffrey Dahmer have their tamer counterparts in patients who will never commit a sexually sadistic crime of any kind…," forensic psychiatrist Robert I. Simon, MD, reports in his book *Bad Men Do What Good Men Dream.* "I have treated solid citizens who mentally torture their spouses, children [and] elderly parents…but would not dream of raising a finger to physically harm anyone."

Yet individuals who physically abuse their spouses or children may well also be sadists, Welner asserts.

And just as cruelty inflicted by infamous sadists can take a heavy toll on victims, this is also the case with cruelty inflicted by everyday sadists.

Stone once treated a college student who had been raised by an abusive aunt and uncle. She got one meal a day while their children got three. She had to fetch sticks for her uncle to beat her. Because of this atrocious treatment, she developed the eating disorder bulimia and several times also attempted to cut herself.

"Steve" worked for a large communications company in Boston. He was emotionally tortured by some fellow workers for two reasons: He earned more money than they did and refused to join their union. On one occasion, they mailed a package containing a dead cat to him. On another, they encircled his house and shouted epithets at him and his wife. As a result, Steve experienced debilitating nightmares, flashbacks, and other symptoms of posttraumatic stress disorder (PTSD) and quit his job. Only two years later, did he feel confident enough to once again enter the workplace.

PASSING JUDGMENT ON THE EVILDOERS IN YOUR LIFE

So how severely should everyday sadists such as those who attacked Steve be judged? Unfortunately, evildoer experts and evildoer research can't really tell us at this point. The same goes for regular folks who engage in bad behavior other than sadism.

Let's say that your boss is harassing you sexually, and you'd like to bring a civil lawsuit against him for this reason. Yet to win such a lawsuit, regardless of which state you live and work in, you have to demonstrate that your boss's actions were outrageous and beyond the bounds of decency. Yet which behaviors are actually outrageous and beyond the bounds of decency? Welner asks. There is no universally accepted definition. Moreover, "'Outrageous' may not necessarily be 'criminal,' or even 'illegal!'"

Cultural differences can also muddy the question of what constitutes appropriate or inappropriate sexual behavior in the workplace. "Kay," a newspaper journalist from the Deep South, was transferred to her newspaper's New York City bureau. There she acquired a boss who was a native New Yorker. Down south, Kay was used to patting the backs of her boss and colleagues, even giving them hugs. When she attempted to engage in such behaviors with her Yankee boss, however, he bristled. She got the message.

And how do evil behaviors that are not sadistic stack up against sadistic behaviors from a moral stance?

Stone once proposed that individuals (usually younger individuals) who engage in school truancy, steal small amounts of money, shoplift, or commit minor acts of vandalism should be judged the least harshly. Then come people who have committed property crimes, people who have committed sexual offenses without violence, con artists and financial criminals. After that come murderers and finally individuals who get a kick out of torturing their victims as well as killing the—in brief, the worst of the worst.

While such a categorization may be generally helpful, it does contain pitfalls, some evildoer experts indicate. For instance, certain financial criminals may have destroyed so many people's lives that they should be judged more severely than say, sadists or murderers.

Then finally comes this question: Can what evildoer experts tell us about whether certain evildoers are more depraved than others help us to make better informed and fairer judgments about individuals who harm us? Quite possibly.

Also, intent and attitude after a crime provide a crucial context for passing judgment that the crime alone can't provide, Welner cautions. Take the case of a man who assaulted a woman carrying groceries, stabbed her to death, then took several bites out of a sandwich he found in her groceries. Such a seemingly trivial action reflected his indifference to the odious act he had just committed, and thus he should be judged more harshly than if he had only assaulted and killed his victim, Welner contends.

The take-home message? When people have harmed us, perhaps we should take into consideration not only what they have done to us, but also their intent and their attitude afterward if we want to judge them justly.

Interestingly, Hilary Clinton appears to have taken this tack regarding her husband Bill's infidelity with White House intern Monica Lewinsky. During an interview with Barbara Walters on ABC TV on June 8, 2003, Hilary reported that one reason why she had forgiven Bill for his transgression is that she had come to understand that what he had done had been the result of moral weakness— not to intentionally hurt her.

FOUR
ARE EVILDOERS "CRAZY"?

On March 30, 1981, President Ronald Reagan didn't have his usual "luck of the Irish." As he emerged from the side door of the Washington Hilton Hotel, facing T Street, NW, a reporter called out a question. Being a "lefty," Reagan raised his left arm. You could then hear rhythmic, high-pitched "cracks," and then people screaming, and smell the acrid, sour stench of gunpowder. A young man mingling with the press had fired six bullets, wounding the president, a secret service agent, a policeman, and White House press secretary James Brady, who collapsed on the pavement, blood dribbling from his skull.

The would-be presidential assassin, John Hinckley, Jr., was arrested, found not guilty by reason of insanity, and imprisoned in St. Elizabeth's [Psychiatric] Hospital in Washington, DC for the next third-of-a-century. Then in the summer of 2016, a federal judge ruled that Hinckley was no longer a threat to others and could leave the hospital to live with his 90-year-old mother. In September 2016, he made the transfer. His mother lived in Kingsmill, a network of small residential villages outside of Williamsburg, Virginia.

However, not all the residents of Kingsmill were happy about the new arrival. As one protested in *The Virginia Gazette:* "How can

Williamsburg officials let him come and stay here when he shot all those people and is crazy?"

Indeed, there is no denying that a number of pernicious, and often grotesque, deeds have been committed by individuals with a serious mental illness that makes them psychotic—that is, distorts their sense of reality. Such illnesses include bipolar disorder, a major depression with psychotic features, postpartum depression, and especially schizophrenia of the paranoid type.

Back in 1975, for example, a Sacramento, California man named Richard Chase was institutionalized for paranoid schizophrenia, but eventually released on the assumption that he was not a danger to society. Several years later, he murdered six people and drank their blood, giving him the moniker "The Vampire of Sacramento."

In 1997, in Harlan, Kentucky, a young man named Gary Stephens murdered his parents, burned their bodies, and then dumped their ashes and bone fragments into the river. He too had paranoid schizophrenia.

Toward the end of 1999, a Brit with paranoid schizophrenia named Michael Abram slipped into the mansion belonging to former Beatle George Harrison, then stabbed Harrison with a knife.

In 2012, a Maryland engineering student named Alexander Kinyua confessed to killing his housemate and then consuming his heart and part of his brain. Kinyua was diagnosed with paranoid schizophrenia and committed to a mental institution.

Furthermore, a spate of recent studies has suggested that people with psychotic disorders are at an increased risk of violence, especially severe violence such as homicide. Here are two examples of such studies, one conducted in Australia and one conducted in Sweden.

Researchers at the Victoria Institute of Forensic Mental Health in Victoria, Australia compared the criminal records of 2,861 schizophrenia patients to the criminal records of an equal number of comparison subjects matched for age, gender, and neighborhood of residence. The patient cohort was drawn from the psychiatric-case registers of the state of Victoria. The comparison subjects were drawn from a database generated from criminal-record searches performed as part of the state's process for selecting people for jury duty.

Compared with the control subjects, the patients with schizophrenia accumulated a greater total number of criminal convictions (8,791 versus 1,119) and were significantly more likely to have been convicted (22 percent versus 8 percent). They were also more likely to have been convicted of an offense involving violence (8 percent versus 2 percent). These results were published in the April 2004 *American Journal of Psychiatry.*

From 1988 to 2000, 1,340 men and 349 women—altogether 1,689 arson offenders—were convicted of arson in Sweden. Swedish and British researchers compared the prevalence of schizophrenia in this cohort to the prevalence of schizophrenia in a large random sample of the Swedish population (40,560 people). After taking sociodemographic factors into consideration that might have skewed their results, the researchers found that the male arsonists were 23 times more likely to have schizophrenia than were men in the general population, and that female arsonists were 39 times more likely to have schizophrenia than were women in the general population.

"These risk estimates are higher than those reported for other violent crimes and place arson in the same category as homicides as crimes that are most strongly associated with psychotic disorders," the researchers concluded in the May 2011 *Schizophrenia Bulletin.*

When psychotic patients engage in violence, sometimes it is precipitated by delusions (false beliefs) and/or auditory hallucinations (voices that really don't exist). For instance, Richard Chase, sited above, drank his victims' blood to replace his own, which he thought was turning into powder. Michael Abram stabbed his Beatles victim because a voice in his head had told him that the Beatles were witches. Gary Stephens killed his parents because he believed that they had been replaced by duplicates that wanted to kill him.

Moreover, a study reported in the March 6, 2013 *JAMA Psychiatry* linked serious violence committed by psychotic individuals with three types of paranoid delusions. They were a feeling of being spied upon, a feeling of being conspired against, and a feeling of being persecuted. Such delusions in turn appear to make the individuals experiencing them angry, and their anger in turn appears to drive them toward serious violence.

Not all researchers who have looked for a link between delusions and serious violence have found such an association, though. Also, clinicians who work with schizophrenia patients know that such patients can experience chronic debilitating delusions or chronic debilitating auditory hallucinations without acting in response to them. Thus, even the experts are not able to predict with any certainty which schizophrenia patients might engage in violence and when.

THE PUBLIC HAS ITS OWN MISCONCEPTION

Because of the often-monstrous nature of homicides committed by people with psychotic disorders, such homicides tend to get a lot of press coverage. This is undoubtedly one of the reasons why so many people believe that anybody who commits such acts must be "deranged," "sick," or "crazy." In fact, this is not the case. Most vile acts—even those that involve appalling cruelty—are *not* carried out by individuals who are seriously mentally ill, scientists have discovered.

For instance, using Swedish national registry data for the years 1988 to 2000, researchers found that individuals with a serious mental illness committed only five percent of the violent crimes in

Sweden. These results appeared in the August 2006 *American Journal of Psychiatry*.

An even more compelling investigation was published in the summer 2010 issue of the *Journal of the American Academy of Psychiatry and the Law*. Several psychologists from the John Jay College of Criminal Justice in New York City examined a national sample of 38 serial sex murderers who had slain some 162 victims altogether. All but one of them had engaged in nauseating rituals such as forcing a victim to cannibalize prior victims or to engage in bestiality with his or her dog. Nonetheless, only two of the murderers had had any symptoms of psychosis, and in those two cases, psychotic symptoms appeared to have not contributed to their nefarious acts.

Several other studies in recent years have produced comparable results.

Forensic experts tend to concur with these findings.

"People with a mental disorder only account for a small proportion of society's violence," Pamela Taylor, MD, a Welsh psychiatrist, told me in 2004.

In a 2011 interview with *Psychiatric News*, Paul Appelbaum, MD, a professor of psychiatry, medicine, and law at Columbia University in New York City, said that overall, the scientific evidence supports the conclusion that individuals with psychotic disorders are at a heightened risk of engaging in violence, especially severe violence as homicide. Nonetheless, he emphasized, "Most people with schizophrenia are not violent, and only a very small fraction of violence in the United States is attributable to mental illness."

Then in December 2012, Wayne LaPierre, CEO of the National Rifle Association, appeared on the television program *Meet the Press*. During his appearance, he referred to people who commit violent crimes as "lunatics." The American Psychiatric Association (APA) quickly issued a press release to rebut his statement. In the release, APA president Dilip Jeste, MD, asserted that LaPierre's statement gave the public the mistaken impression that all dire deeds are committed by people who are mentally ill, whereas in fact "only four to five percent of violent crimes are committed by people with mental illness." And in the release, APA's CEO, Jay Scully, MD, added: "The idea that mental illness and evil are one and the same thing is simply a relic of the past and has no place in our public dialogue."

So, if most atrocious deeds are not committed by the seriously mentally ill, then who *is* responsible for them? A Finnish study reported in the May 2003 *American Journal of Psychiatry* provides a thought-provoking answer.

Between 1982 and 1992, 132 Finnish women were convicted of murder or attempted murder. Researchers followed them up over the next 18 years to see how many would re-offend, and who they were. About a quarter of the women re-offended during the follow-up period. Yet of this quarter, only 10 percent had a psychotic disorder, but 81 percent had disordered personalities. In other words, they possessed quirky personalities that deviate from what most of us have or perhaps personality traits that many of us have, but in an extreme form.

People with disordered personalities are usually unlikeable and irritating, and in the opinion of personality expert C. Robert Cloninger, MD., a professor of psychiatry and genetics at Washington University in Saint Louis, they have "a deficit in their spiritual perspective, which leads to patterns of thought, feeling, and behavior that can be described as vices like pride, lust, and greed."

One of the disordered personalities that have been linked with evildoing is the schizoid personality. Such individuals tend to be aloof, loners; to experience strange thoughts; to have difficulty separating

LET'S TOAST TO YOUR DEATH

What do serial killers use to prep themselves for the kill? Often alcohol or drugs. A study of 95 serial sex killers found that almost half had abused alcohol or used illicit substances such as cocaine, LSD, or amphetamines. Moreover, most of those who abused alcohol imbibed it right before raping or murdering in order to kindle their hate or rev up their lust for revenge.

Robert Hanlon, MD, a Northwestern University psychiatrist, studied the forensic histories of 77 men convicted of murder and imprisoned either in Illinois or Missouri. Nearly all of the men who had killed impulsively, and most of the men who had killed after forethought had a history of alcohol or drug abuse and/or were under the influence of alcohol or drugs at the time.

Although adult arsonists can cause a devastating loss in property and lives, very little was known about them for many years. Then the 2001-2002 National Epidemiological o Survey on Alcohol and Related Conditions—a nationally representative sample of some 43,000 Americans aged 18 and older – gave some scientists an unprecedented opportunity to learn more about adult arsonists. The reason? One of the many questions asked of those surveyed was this: "In your entire life, did you ever start a fire on purpose to destroy someone's property or just to see it burn?"

Out of some 43,000 survey respondents, some 400 individuals answered yes to this question, the scientists reported in the July 10, 2009 *Comprehensive Psychiatry*. Thus, extrapolating from this finding, it looks as if arsonists constitute one percent of the American population.

Moreover, by comparing survey responses from some 400 individuals who reported having intentionally started fires to those from the some 43,000 individuals who had not, the scientists were able to glean some valuable insights into adult arsonists. One was that arsonists are 12 times more likely to have antisocial personality disorder than are people who do not set fires. Another was that they tend to engage in a wide swath of other despicable behaviors besides arson such as assault, robbery, rape, and cruelty to animals. And a third was that they often abuse alcohol.

Alcohol and drugs can likewise up the ante that seriously mentally ill individuals will engage in acts that are a grave threat to society. Duke University researchers studied some 800 individuals with a serious mental illness to determine how many had engaged in violent behavior during the previous year. Thirteen percent had, the researchers found. The researchers then looked to see which demographic, social, environmental, or clinical factors might have contributed to such behavior. Three important factors emerged: having been victimized by violence, currently being exposed to violence, and abusing alcohol or drugs.

Some 12,000 people were born in the northern part of Finland back in 1966. Thanks to Finland's outstanding recordkeeping system, their mental health and criminal records could be tracked over the next quarter-century. Finnish researchers used this data to see which ones committed violent crimes. Most of those who did, it turned out, had schizophrenia *and* abused substances.

"I think that there is little doubt that patients with schizophrenia who develop command delusions or hallucinations are a danger to themselves or others if they are not medicated, and particularly if they turn to alcohol and other drugs to medicate themselves," Darrel Regier, MD, declared while serving as director of research at the APA.

In contrast, the seriously mentally ill who *do not* abuse substances account for barely three percent of murders, evildoer expert Michael Stone, MD, remarks.

Then there are those people who have both a serious mental illness *and* a personality disorder as well as those people who have a serious mental illness *plus* a personality disorder *and* who abuse substances in addition. Either combination, but especially the latter, can be lethal as far as public safety is concerned.

Jessica Ferranti, MD, an assistant clinical professor of psychiatry at the University of California at Davis, and her coworkers reviewed the medical records of 47 women who had committed murders yet had been found not guilty by reason of insanity between 1999 and 2005. Ferranti and her colleagues selected a random sample of 47 men who had committed murders yet been found not guilty by reason of insanity during the same period and compared their medical records to those of the 47 women.

All of the subjects, the researchers learned, had a serious mental illness, notably schizophrenia or schizoaffective disorder, which is schizophrenia combined with some affective symptoms. All the subjects also had a personality disorder, especially antisocial personality disorder in the men and especially borderline personality disorder, which is characterized by emotional instability, fear of abandonment, and suicidal behavior, in the women. And over a third of both female and male subjects had been abusing substances at the time of their offense.

Indeed, when individuals have both a serious mental illness and a disordered personality, or both a serious mental illness plus a disordered personality *and* abuse substances, they can not only endanger society, but challenge it in another way as well.

MAD, BAD, OR BOTH?

For a Chicago teen named Ted Kaczynski, 1958 was a very good year. Although Kaczynski came from a modest background, he was highly intelligent, and Harvard University accepted him even though he was only 16 years of age. In 1962, he graduated from Harvard and then moved on to the University of Michigan at Ann Arbor, where he obtained a master's degree and a doctorate in mathematics. In 1967, he was hired as an assistant professor of mathematics at the University of California at Berkeley.

At this point, however, his life took a nosedive. His students at Berkeley rated him poorly because of his aloofness. In 1969, he resigned his position at Berkeley and moved to the wilds of Montana, where he built himself a cabin without electricity and running water and sustained himself as a sort of prehistoric hunter-gatherer. There he remained for the next quarter-century until Federal Bureau of Investigation (FBI) agents finally determined that he was the infamous "Unabomber" responsible for a swath of bombings and mail bombings from the late 1970s to the mid-1990s that killed three people and wounded 23 others.

When FBI agents arrested him at his cabin on April 3, 1996, Kaczynski resembled a prehistoric human. His brown hair was long and wild, his greying beard grizzled. His body was filthy and smelled repugnant. Then there were his eyes: They didn't look at you, but through you, into what appeared to be a dark and desolate world.

During 1997 and 1998, a number of forensic experts examined Kaczynski before he went to trial. Those testifying for the defense argued that he had paranoid schizophrenia. Those testifying for the prosecution argued that he had a paranoid personality disorder with a number of antisocial traits.

Kaczynski's trial illustrates some of the challenges facing jurors when they have to decide whether a criminal defendant's acts were prompted by a serious mental illness or by a defective personality/character.

First off, they are faced with a question that flummoxes most of us, even the most erudite or worldly. For instance, Bill O'Reilly, author and former host of the television show The O'Reilly Factor, invited evildoer expert Michael Welner, MD, to appear on his show on April 18, 2007 in the wake of some school shootings. During the discussion, O'Reilly asked Welner: "Can somebody be mentally ill and evil at the same time?" "Absolutely!" Welner replied.

But even if jurors accept Welner's premise that a defendant can be both mad and bad, they are still faced with the vexing question of whether he carried out his heinous act because of his mental illness or because of his depraved personality/character. As Welsh forensic psychiatrist Pamela Taylor, MD, explained to me: "When people have 'pure' psychosis and are manifestly driven to some dreadful act by their symptoms, then it is relatively easy to satisfy…a court that not only are the disorder and violence related, but also the violence follows from the disorder…[But] when the person already has an established pattern of antisocial behavior – and perhaps violence – and there is no clear symptom link, it is certainly more difficult to judge how far a mental disorder may be leading to an impairment of capacity/responsibility for the act."

However, a possible guideline for jurors in such a difficult situation may lie in a study published in the June 30, 2007 *Law and Human Behavior.*

The researchers focused on 1,455 adult schizophrenia subjects and looked to see which ones had engaged in antisocial behaviors before age 15. The answer was 488; the rest had not. After that, the researchers determined which of the subjects had engaged in violence during the previous six months. Finally, the researchers compared the rate of violence within the preceding six months for the early antisocial group to the rate of violence within the preceding six months for those who had not been antisocial early in life. The rate was twice as high for the former as for the latter—28 percent versus 14 percent.

Thus, it looked as if those subjects who had been antisocial from an early age were especially prone to violence, and that their antisocial personality/character not their schizophrenia—was what had prompted them to become violent.

Therefore, if a criminal defendant were both seriously mentally ill and had a disordered personality, the presence or absence of antisocial behavior in his youth might possibly help jurors decide whether his mental illness or depraved personality/character led to his offense.

Whether this is so or not, though, the challenge for jurors could become even more daunting in those cases where a criminal defendant is not only seriously mentally ill and not only has a disordered personality, but abuses alcohol or drugs.

Let's say that the jurors decide that mental illness was the cause. Then they might well conclude that he was not morally accountable. But if they decide that his personality/character were the cause, then they would probably hold him morally answerable. Yet how about substance abuse? Should he be held morally responsible for that? Probably. For as evildoer expert Michael Stone, MD, has observed, a person could presumably have chosen *not* to get drunk and therefore chosen *not* to have committed whatever act of violence he carried out under the influence.

Now, let's shift the focus a bit. Suppose a person who is seriously mentally ill, but without any personality disorder or substance abuse, commits a depraved act. You would think that it would be easy for jurors to blame his behavior on his mental illness and find him not morally accountable for what he did, right? But not necessarily!

In June 2001, a Texas woman named Andrea Yates drowned her five children in the bathtub, one after the other, then called the police to show them what she had done. She was arrested for the murders and went on trial for them in March 2002. Her attorneys and family argued that she had committed the murders in the wake of a serious postpartum depression and had done so to save her children from Satan. The prosecutors concurred that she was seriously mentally ill, but claimed that when she carried out the murders, she was able to tell right from wrong. Thus she should be found guilty of the murders, not innocent because of insanity, they argued. In less than four hours, the jury reached a verdict and concurred with them.

California forensic psychiatrist Park Dietz, MD, PhD, was the star witness for the prosecution in this trial. One might think that Dietz would have been gratified by the jury's finding Yates guilty. But in an interview with *The New York Times* on April 23, 2002, he confessed that he had been troubled by the case both professionally and personally because of the intricacies involved. Yes, he said, Yates was "clearly seriously disturbed," but at the same time, "The weight of the evidence was that it was wrong when she drowned her children." So, should she be held responsible for what she did or not? Well, that depended on *where* she was being tried, and that, Dietz said, is what really bothered him.

Under Texas law, Dietz explained, the jury was essentially compelled to find Yates guilty rather than "not guilty by reason of insanity" because she had committed the killings while knowing her conduct was wrong. Yet "I think I would have found her insane in a jurisdiction where the test is whether she emotionally appreciated the wrongfulness of her actions," Dietz said. "And I certainly would have found her insane in a jurisdiction with [a] rule that a defendant is insane if the crime is the product of a mental disease."

But the story didn't end there. Dietz reported to the court that he had made a mistake during his testimony. Consequently, Yates received a new trial and this time was found not guilty by reason of insanity.

And there is even more to consider when deciding whether Yates should have been found guilty or not. A *60 Minutes* television segment aired on December 9, 2001 was devoted to the Yates case. During this segment, viewers learned that Yates had been advised by doctors after her fourth child that if she had a fifth child, she would once again experience postpartum psychosis. Nonetheless, she decided to ignore the warning and go ahead and have a fifth child. And sure enough, she once again experienced postpartum psychosis. But this time she went further—killing all five children in the throes of the psychosis. So, since she ignored medical advice about not having any more children, thereby incurring psychotic depression, did this action make her answerable for her children's deaths?

And if the Yates case isn't boggling enough from a moral and judicial viewpoint, the following bizarre, but true case is undoubtedly even more so.

THE MAN WHO KILLED THE LOVE OF HIS LIFE

By all accounts, 42-year-old "Greg" was living the all-American dream. He was well-educated, an electrical engineer whom some described as a "wiry nerd" with a master's degree in Business Administration (MBA) to his credit as well. He was employed by a large company and earned good money. He had been married for 20 years to "Nancy," his high school sweetheart and the only woman he had ever dated. They had two teenage children. Moreover, being Mormons, they were leading a healthy lifestyle, consuming neither alcohol nor drugs.

One day, however, his fortune turned when his boss saddled him and his team with an enormous, expensive project that he doubted they could complete in the time allowed. He started sleeping poorly, his stomach churned in disarray. By the time June 22 came, his worst fears were becoming a reality: They would never be able to complete the project by the deadline, which was only three days away.

On that fateful evening, Greg talked with Nancy about what he should do. Should he go to his boss and concede failure? Nancy didn't think so. "How about asking for a deadline extension and more staff to help you with the project?" she suggested. He gave her a goodnight kiss, retired to his home office to use the computer, and then, at 10 p.m., fell into bed exhausted, frazzled, and still undecided about which tack to take.

Several hours later, he was awakened by barking dogs and strange voices. He jumped out of bed and rushed downstairs. Police were present, and to his consternation, they handcuffed him, led him out to a squad car, and drove him to the police station. Snippets of conversation indicated that something bad at happened to Nancy. Only when he was interrogated at the police station, did he learn that that was indeed the case: Nancy had been stabbed 44 times and her body thrown into the backyard swimming pool. And if that wasn't enough, they told him that they were booking him for murdering Nancy since a neighbor had seen him shoving her body into the pool, and since blood had been found on his clothes.

"That can't be!" he bellowed. "Why would I have murdered Nancy? She was my best friend and the love of my life. And I certainly did *not* drag her body into our pool. The neighbor must have mistaken me for somebody else!"

When Greg talked privately with his defense lawyer, he continued to maintain his innocence. The lawyer was inclined to believe him. But if so, then what could be the explanation for these strange and tragic events? A way-out possibility crossed the lawyer's mind: Could Greg have killed Nancy while sleepwalking? If so, it would explain why he had no recollection of either murdering her or of dumping her body into the pool.

The lawyer decided to do some research to see whether sleepwalking might be a credible hypothesis. Indeed, some of Greg's relatives reported that Greg had been a sleepwalker as a child, and that sleepwalking ran in the family. Moreover, a criminal case that had occurred in Canada a few years earlier eerily mirrored Greg's in many ways.

The accused had had no apparent motive, no history of violence, yet had experienced an extended period of psychological stress and insomnia before the attack. The attack occurred shortly after he went to sleep. He had made no attempt to cover up his crime. He claimed that he had no memory of what he had done. But most heartening was the discovery that the accused had been found *not guilty* of murder because he had carried it out in a sleepwalking state.

Greg's lawyer decided to use sleepwalking as his defense tactic for Greg as well. He gathered still more evidence to buttress it, such as having Greg undergo a neurological exam and psychological tests by a court-appointed psychologist and be evaluated by a sleepwalking expert.

Once Greg's trial was underway, it seemed to go well for the defense, especially because the prosecution didn't present any other plausible explanation than sleepwalking for why Greg had killed his wife, such as marital discord or infidelity. But the jury didn't buy the sleepwalking story. It convicted Greg of first-degree murder.

So, was Greg mad, bad, both, or neither? What is your assessment?

FIVE

MEAN GENES OR
A TOXIC ENVIRONMENT?

James Fallon, PhD, is a professor of psychiatry and human behavior at the University of California-Irvine. He's a big guy, of both Sicilian and English descent, with a lion-size head, bushy eyebrows, flashing brown eyes, ruddy cheekbones, and a salt-and-pepper beard. He comes across as both earthy and keenly intelligent.

Although he has studied various aspects of the human brain, he is especially interested in the brains and genetics of criminals.

Back in 2006, Fallon's mother mentioned to him that there had been some bad apples in his family tree (on his father's side) and suggested that he might like to learn more about them. He followed up on her suggestion and, can you believe it, learned that his great-grandfather Thomas Cornell had been hanged in 1667 for murder, and that the subsequent line of Cornells had produced seven other alleged murderers, including the infamous Lizzy Borden. (Lizzy was accused, and controversially acquitted, of killing her father and stepmother with an ax in Fall River, Massachusetts in 1882.)

Fallon was astonished. And somewhat concerned. *Could one of my family members be a born killer?* he wondered. The thought wasn't so way out since heredity *can* influence evildoing, a small, but growing cadre of research attests.

For example, from the 1950s through the 1980s, various researchers had looked to see whether there was a greater concordance rate between identical twins than there was between fraternal twins as far as criminal behavior was concerned. If so, it would suggest that heredity influences criminal behavior more than the environment does since identical twins share 100 percent of their genes, whereas fraternal twins share only 50 percent of theirs. A meta-analysis of these studies, published in 1990, indicated that heredity had a greater influence.

A few years later, Welsh researchers conducted a twin study that came to the same conclusion. Their cohort included 254 twin pairs (508 subjects). Some of the twins were identical, the others fraternal. The subjects were rated as far as conduct problems were concerned not just by their parents and teachers, but by themselves. The researchers looked to see whether there was a greater concordance between identical twins than between fraternal twins insofar as conduct difficulties were concerned. The answer was an unqualified yes. In fact, it suggested that as much as 75 percent of conduct problems could be attributed to heredity, and only 25 percent to environmental factors. These results appeared in the May 2004 issue of the *Archives of General Psychiatry*.

And then there were some Danish researchers who undertook an adoption study to explore the possible impact of inheritance on base behavior. In this study of some 3,700 adopted boys, those whose biological parents (usually fathers) had been convicted of crimes were more likely themselves to be convicted of crimes than were those whose biological parents had had no brush with the law, In contrast, those boys whose adoptive parents had been convicted of crimes were no more likely to be convicted of crimes than were those boys whose adoptive parents had had no brush with the law. These findings once again indicted heredity as a major player in pernicious behavior.

CHROMOSOMAL EVIDENCE BOLSTERS THE ARGUMENT

Normally women's sex- chromosome machinery consists of two "X-chromosomes and men's of one "X" and one "Y." But once in a while this pattern gets messed up. For instance, a man might possess one X and two YY's or two X's and one Y instead of the usual XY.

There had been some reason to think that men with the sex chromosome abnormality XYY or the sex chromosome abnormality XXY commit criminal acts more than men with the normal XY combination do. Two psychiatric researchers at the Royal Edinburgh Hospital in Scotland decided to explore this possibility.

Some 34,000 newborns in Scotland had been screened at birth for sex chromosome abnormalities. The researchers used this database to identify 17 male newborns who had the XYY sex chromosome pattern and 17 who had the XXY one. The researchers located the 34 individuals, who were now teens or young men, and determined whether they had experienced any criminal convictions. The researchers compared their results to those for 60 control subjects.

The XYY men (but not the XXY men) were found to have experienced more criminal convictions than the controls.

Thus, men with the XYY sex chromosome pattern may have a slightly increased liability for antisocial behavior, the researchers reported in the July 1999 *Psychological Medicine.*

And along the same lines, but more recently, German forensic psychiatrists reported that of 13 men arrested for sexual sadistic homicide, three had the XYY chromosome abnormality. So even though the XYY chromosomal pattern is rare, it could still contribute to some of society's depravity, evildoer expert Michael Stone, MD, opines.

MOLECULAR GENETICS ADDS AMMUNITION

Molecular genetics research adds even more ammunition to the contention that heredity can influence evildoing.

Tatiana Foroud, PhD, an associate professor of medical and molecular genetics and psychiatry at Indiana University, and her colleagues were able to link a gene on chromosome 2 and another on chromosome 19 with childhood conduct problems. The one on chromosome 2 is especially interesting. It has been linked with alcohol dependence, and childhood conduct problems in turn are a strong risk factor for alcohol abuse. So, "taken together, these findings suggest that some of the genes contributing to alcohol dependence in adulthood may also contribute to conduct disorder in childhood," Foroud and her colleagues proposed in the January 2004 *Molecular Psychiatry*.

Another gene variant that has been implicated in wanton behavior is located on chromosome 4. This finding comes from Joel Gelernter, MD, a professor of psychiatry at Yale University, and colleagues and was published in the April 15, 2012 *Biological Psychiatry*. Their research was based on 4,679 subjects, 567 of whom had been diagnosed with antisocial personality disorder. All were genotyped, and genes found in individuals with the disorder were compared with those found in individuals without. A specific variant of a gene dubbed COL25A1 was found to be present significantly more often in the disorder group than in the latter, especially when accompanied by substance dependence. Moreover, the researchers were able to replicate this finding in another large sample of subjects—3,413 individuals. Thus this particular gene version may well be complicit in depravity.

Now enter dopamine, a nerve transmitter in the brain that is known to be involved in, among other things, impulsive and addictive behaviors. A particular version of a gene that makes the dopamine receptor has been linked not just with alcoholism and pathological gambling, but with base behavior in both youth and adults. Moreover, a high-activity variant of a gene that makes an enzyme involved in dopamine metabolism has been coupled with the most severe, persistent type of antisocial behavior. This is antisocial behavior that starts in childhood and is usually accompanied by attention-deficit/hyperactivity disorder (ADHD). The enzyme is called catechol-O-methyltransferase (COMT).

And there's more. The nerve transmitter serotonin is best known for its feel-good effects. Many antidepressants counter depression by increasing serotonin levels in the brain. However, a paucity in serotonin has also been implicated in impulsive aggression leading to suicide or antisocial behavior, and these negative effects in turn appear to be unleashed, at least in part, by particular versions of genes coding for serotonin receptors, serotonin transporters, an enzyme involved in serotonin synthesis, and, as you will see, even an enzyme involved in the metabolism of serotonin.

FINALLY, A MOST INFAMOUS GENE VARIANT

During the 1980s, Dutch genetic researchers got wind of a multi-generational family where a handful of its members were doing weird things. Some responded with angry outbursts if they were afraid or frustrated. Others engaged in even more egregious behaviors involving impulsive aggression, such as arson, exhibitionism, or attempted rape. What, for heaven's sake, was going on? Could there be a common genetic explanation for all of these individuals' untoward behaviors? The researchers suspected that there might be, and that it might concern a gene that makes an enzyme called monoamine oxidase A (MAOA). This enzyme is known to metabolize not just serotonin, but two other neurotransmitters—dopamine and norepinephrine. Both animal and human studies have linked low MAOA activity with aggression and antisocial behaviors.

The researchers evaluated MAOA enzyme activity in the subjects of interest and found that it was totally nonexistent. They then evaluated the gene that makes the enzyme and found that it contained a mutation and was thus abnormal. Thus, it looked as though this defective MAOA gene variant made a defective MAOA enzyme that was totally inactive, and somehow this inactivity caused, or at least contributed to, the subjects' impulsive aggression and undesirable behaviors.

In brief, it looked as if a specific gene could change human behavior –something that had never been demonstrated—and for the worse.

These provocative findings were reported in the October 22, 1993 *Science*. As it turned out, this gene mutation is exceedingly rare. But a lot of evidence has accrued that another variant of the MAOA gene is very common. This maverick version produces some MAOA enzyme, but an insufficient amount. This low-activity MAOA gene variant has also been linked with antisocial behavior. In fact, there is probably more evidence indicating it in evildoing than any other at this point.

Take a look:

Australian researchers tested 210 subjects who had either the low-activity MAOA gene variant or the high-activity one, that is, the normal version, for antisocial personality traits and emotional reaction to a threatening situation. The low-activity group scored considerably higher on such traits, as well as on anger when faced with threat. So whenever people with the low-activity variant feel threatened, they may react excessively with anger, and this rage in turn may prompt them to do vile things, the researchers suspect.

Scientists at the National Institute of Mental Health in Bethesda, Maryland came up with comparable findings. They focused on 142 subjects who had inherited either the low-activity MAOA gene variant or the high one. They used brain scans to look at the subjects' brains while the subjects were subjected to certain emotion-provoking tasks, then compared the results for the two groups. The low-activity group showed a greater response in two emotion-related brain structures, the amygdala and hippocampus, and at the same time, a lesser response in impulse-control areas in the frontal brain. These results appeared February 4, 2009 in the online version of *Neuropsychopharmacology*.

And while having the low-activity MAOA gene variant is not *de rigueur* for gang membership, it sure may help, another inquiry headed by Kevin Beaver, PhD, an assistant professor of criminology at Florida State University, indicates. Beaver and his team not only found that gang members are more likely to have the low-activity MAOA gene variant than the high-activity one, but that those gang members who use weapons in a fight are even more likely to have it than are members who are less violent. "We weren't surprised that the gene predicted violence and gang membership for the full sample," Beaver told me, "but that the MAOA gene could distinguish the most violent gang members from the less violent gang members was surprising."

So, all things considered, it looks as if the low-activity MAOA gene variant is truly a mean gene.

A HOUSE OF HORRORS

When a Texan named Tommy Lynn Sells was a child during the 1960s, his mother turned him over to an aunt to raise, and the aunt then passed him on to a pedophile who sexually abused him. These experiences filled him with a volcanic hatred for these three people. They also prompted him to seek revenge against people who resembled them.

For instance, he would slip into the homes of young women, slit their throats, and gloat as the blood flowed out of them. When he came across a man sexually abusing a child, he killed him. In 1999, in Del Rio, Texas, he slit the throats of two girls, but one of them survived and was able to describe him to the police. Her description led to his apprehension.

In 2000, Sells was tried and convicted of murder and given the death sentence. He was incarcerated in a prison near Livingston, Texas. When evildoer expert Michael Stone, MD, visited Sells on death row in 2007, Sells told Stone that he was convinced that the early abuse he had experienced had contributed tremendously to who he had become.

Indeed, of all the evidence linking environmental factors with malign behavior – and the evidence is considerably more robust than that linking heredity to such behavior – it points to childhood abuse as a major contributor.

Boys who experience abuse have been found to be at risk of conduct disorder, antisocial personality symptoms, and becoming violent offenders. The earlier children experience mishandling, the more likely they are to develop such problems.

Most serial killers experienced severe physical and sexual mal-treatment, evildoer expert Robert I. Simon, MD, reports. Stone concurs. Of the serial killers he has studied, a great number came from "horrific backgrounds, where they were brutalized by one or both parents," Stone told me. Moreover, two-thirds had been emotionally abused. One, for instance, was mocked by both parents because he stuttered. Another was jeered by his mother and stepfather: They called him "Pissy Pants" because of his bed wetting.

Federal Bureau of Investigation (FBI) profiler Roy Hazelwood interviewed 41 convicted rapists and found that 76 percent had been sexually victimized as youngsters. One, "Tim," reported that when he was seven years old, his mother had hired a "knockout babysitter, who taught me how to go down on her." Another, "Hank," described how he had been repeatedly raped by his father until he was age 11. After that, his father, a serial rapist, started taking him along to hunt for prey. Furthermore, a remarkably large number of pedophiles were themselves sexual abused as children, various studies and reports have found.

Yet even if childhood ill treatment is a major catalyst of depraved behavior, a number of other environmental factors have been found capable of contributing to it as well.

One is smoking during pregnancy. The finding comes from a study headed by Patricia Brennan, PhD, an assistant professor of psychology at Emory University in Atlanta, and published in the January 2002 *American Journal of Psychiatry.*

Brennan and her colleagues used as their subjects some 8,000 individuals who had been born in Copenhagen, Denmark between 1959 and 1961. Extensive demographic and medical information had been gathered for each of these individuals before, during, and after their births and recorded. For instance, whether the fathers of the individuals had a criminal history had been determined from the Danish criminal register. Whether the fathers or mothers of the individuals had ever been hospitalized for psychiatric or substance-abuse reasons was ascertained from the Danish psychiatric register. And whether the mothers of any of the individuals had smoked during the last three months of pregnancy was gleaned from interviews with the mothers during pregnancy or shortly after delivery.

Brennan and her coworkers then ascertained, in 1994, which of the 8,000 individuals had gone on, as adults, to engage in criminal acts. Their source was the Danish criminal register. Subsequently they used the data that had been collected about the 8,000 subjects back in 1959-61 and the data they had themselves collected in 1994 to answer this question: Was there a link between maternal smoking during the last three months of pregnancy and offspring committing crimes? The answer was a resounding yes, even though they had taken into consideration socioeconomic status, pregnancy complications, parents' psychiatric or substance abuse problems, or other factors that might have distorted their results. And even more disturbing: The more cigarettes mothers had smoked during the last three months of pregnancy, the greater the chance that their offspring would become criminals.

Alcohol consumption during pregnancy may likewise set unborn children up for later wrongdoing, University of Minnesota researchers reported in the December 2008 *Pediatrics*. They evaluated 1,252 adolescents for conduct disorder. They also interviewed the youngsters' mothers to learn whether they had drunk any alcohol while pregnant with them, and if so, how much. They looked to see whether there was any connection between alcohol use during pregnancy and offspring's later conduct problems, while taking into consideration some possibly confounding factors, such as whether the mother had smoked during pregnancy or whether the mother or father was engaging in antisocial behaviors. There was indeed a link, they found. Even as few as three drinks a week during pregnancy appeared to unleash conduct disorder symptoms.

DEPRESSED PARENTS MAY UP THE RISK

I have a childhood friend who still recalls, after so many years, how she would come home from school and find her mother still in her nightgown and the house a mess. Was her mother depressed?

Probably, my friend thinks. In any event, it was as if her mother was in another world and both emotionally and physically was unavailable to her. And it hurt. And still does.

Fortunately, my friend did not experience any major psychological damage from her mother's depression and neglect. But some children do, and the damage in turn may set them up for depravity, studies have found.

In one, some thousand seventh and eighth graders were followed up to age 18 to find out whether any engaged in antisocial behaviors. The researchers examined the ways whereby those who had engaged in antisocial behaviors had been raised. Many had had depressed parents, it turned out, and parental depression in turn appeared to have contributed to their unfavorable outcomes.

In another, of over 1,000 American families, researchers evaluated the mothers to determine whether any were depressed or whether any were depressed and engaging in antisocial behaviors. The researchers also determined whether the offspring of these two groups had conduct problems themselves and compared both groups. The children whose mothers were both depressed and antisocial had dramatically higher rates of conduct problems than the children of mothers who were depressed only. The reasons? Compared with the depressed-only mothers, the depressed-antisocial mothers often had financial problems, drinking problems, or experienced domestic violence. As a result, they were especially incapable of giving their youngsters the attention and emotional warmth they craved and especially likely to physically abuse them.

Actually youngsters who have highly antisocial fathers are less likely to become antisocial if their fathers are absent rather than present in their lives, another inquiry found.

And could it be that the offspring of any parent whose past is marred by murder and mayhem might be better off if not raised by that parent?

A chilling story out of Modesto, California appears to illustrate this point.

A woman named Jackie Peterson experienced a dismal childhood. Her father was murdered when she was two years old. She was reared in an orphanage. As a single woman, she had two children, Anne and Don, whom she gave up for adoption.

In 1997, when Anne was 32 years old, she met her biological mother Jackie for the first time. Jackie learned that Anne had had wonderful adoptive parents and that her life had turned out fine. Anne learned that Jackie had eventually married a man named Lee Peterson; that they had had a son together, Scott; and that Jackie thought Scott was wonderful. Eventually Anne met her step-brother Scott as well. She found him "charismatic, charming, courteous, and polite."

Scott, however, also had a dark side. Although he was married to a lovely young woman, Laci, and she was pregnant with their son, he had apparently found another woman more to his liking and decided to kill both Laci and his unborn son. He carried out the act on Christmas Eve 2002. Ironically, his mother's father had also been murdered before Christmas. Could it be that he had learned that detail from his mother, and that it had helped him map out his own nefarious plan? And how would Scott's life have turned out if he, like his stepsister Anne, had not been exposed to his biological mother's influence while growing up? Would he still have become a murderer? We will never know. But it's a possibility.

In any event, parental absence is not always a panacea for evil-doing. On the contrary, it sometimes provokes it, a large Finnish study suggests.

The investigation was based on a vast amount of socioeconomic, health, and crime information that had been collected about some 5,000 women from birth up to 32 years of age. The researchers focused on those women who had become criminals, then zoomed in to determine which factor or factors in their backgrounds most strongly predicted such an outcome. The absence of a father during childhood was the strongest predictor: Women who had lacked a father were almost three times more likely to become a criminal than were women who had had one.

Not surprisingly, the lack of a father can also pave the way for boys to pursue a life of crime, the same researchers found, but in a separate study.

This cohort consisted of some 5,000 men who had been followed from birth up to 32 years of age, as had the women in the above-mentioned study, so that a lot was known about their backgrounds and their current lives. The researchers looked to see whether prenatal or perinatal risk factors such as a mother's smoking or drinking during pregnancy or a premature birth, as well as being an only child or not having a father present, could be linked with later criminal activity. The researchers were especially interested in the only-child question, and for several reasons. Only children often lack the social skills that children with siblings have. Children without social skills are often rejected by their peers. And peer rejection in turn is known to be a risk factor for antisocial behavior.

As the researchers suspected, being an only child did seem to have an impact on whether a boy later became a criminal because men who had been an only child turned out to be twice as likely to commit a violent crime as were men who had had siblings. But the results showed something even more troubling. If a man had not only been an only child, but had also been exposed to prenatal or perinatal risk factors, it increased his chances of committing a violent crime fourfold. And if he had not only been an only child, but had lacked a father, it increased his odds eightfold.

Now, suppose being an only child and having an absent father is compounded by maternal neglect and marital discord. What happens then? The consequences could be deadly, as you will see.

BLEACHED BONES AND CANNIBALISM

His name was Jeffrey Dahmer. He was born in Milwaukee, Wisconsin in 1960. His mother worked as a teletype machine instructor. His father, Lionel Dahmer, was studying for a degree in chemistry at Marquette University and was rarely home. By the time Jeffrey entered first grade, his mother was spending more and more time in bed, demanding constant attention whenever her husband was present. Moreover, the parents were constantly bickering; the house bristled with tension. Jeffrey's first-grade teacher wrote on his report card that she had the impression that he felt neglected.

In 1966, Jeffrey's father got his degree in chemistry, and the family relocated to Ohio as his father had found employment as an analytical chemist there. In 1970, Lionel was concerned about Jeffrey's lethargic attitude and solitary existence. So, when Jeffrey asked him how to bleach chicken bones, Lionel willingly showed him, thinking that his interest arose from scientific curiosity.

As Jeffrey entered puberty, he came to realize that he was gay. He also started fantasizing about dominating and controlling subservient gay partners, and these fantasies somehow became intertwined with his fantasies about dissecting dead animals. In 1977, when he was 17 years old, he also started drinking heavily. In 1978, his parents divorced, and both moved out of the house. Since Jeffrey was 18 years old at this point, he was legally considered an adult and not subject to court custodial considerations. He continued to live in the house alone.

That summer, Jeffrey picked up a male hitchhiker, lured him to his house, bludgeoned him, strangled him to death, masturbated over his corpse, and then dismembered it. But that was only a start. During the next 13 years, Jeffrey raped, murdered, and dismembered 16 more men or boys.

And if that wasn't macabre enough, he also cut up their bodies and stored various body parts in his refrigerator for later use. For instance, he would use genitals as an aphrodisiac to enhance his sexual pleasure during masturbation. He would sprinkle biceps and hearts with meat tenderizer, fry them in cooking oil, add steak sauce, and then eat them for dinner in the belief that they would make him stronger. The biceps tasted as delicious as steak, he later commented, but the hearts were spongy and rather tasteless—not to be recommended.

Eventually Jeffrey's feasting on human remains came to an end when he was arrested, tried, convicted, and given four life sentences in prison. He was ultimately murdered by a prison inmate.

The paternal absence, maternal neglect, and parental discord Jeffrey experienced as a youth undoubtedly contributed to his heinous deeds. And that he was an only child for the first six years of his life—he acquired a baby brother after that—probably had an impact as well. Yet it's hard to believe that these factors alone could have triggered his nefarious behaviors. After all, he had been spared some other well-documented environmental risks for evildoing, such as emotional, physical, or sexual abuse; inconsistent discipline; a low socioeconomic status, neighborhood violence, or gang membership. So, could it be that, in addition to paternal absence, maternal neglect, marital discord, and being an only child during the first six years of life, he had inherited one or more genes that had nudged him toward such ghastly acts?

His father Lionel thought so. Lionel wrote in his book *A Father's Story*:" As a scientist, I wonder if this potential for great evil…resides deep in the blood that some of us fathers and mothers may pass on to our children at birth."

MEAN GENES CONSPIRE WITH A TOXIC ENVIRONMENT

Childhood misuse, as we've seen, is a powerful catalyst for pernicious behaviors later in life. But most mishandled children do not pursue a life of depravity. Could the MAOA gene be a decisive factor?

During the late 1990s, when the low-activity MAOA gene variant was gaining notoriety, Avshalom Caspi, PhD, a scientist at the Institute of Psychiatry, King's College, London, and some colleagues asked themselves this question.

Moreover, they decided to conduct a study to answer it.

They incorporated their particular investigation into a much larger one that had been taking place in Dunedin, New Zealand since the 1970's. The Dunedin Study, as it was called, included some 1,000 subjects (half male and half female) who had been evaluated regarding a vast number of health and developmental issues every few years since the age of three. One of the issues was maltreatment. All the subjects were now age 26 and about to be assessed once again for the study.

Caspi and his coworkers used only the male subjects from the Dunedin study—442 men—for their particular inquiry. First, they scoured the Dunedin Study database to learn which of the men had been ill treated as children. Thirty-six percent had been. They then set things up so that all the men, in addition to undergoing their usual Dunedin Study tests, be genotyped for the MAOA gene. Meanwhile, they searched police records in New Zealand and Australia to learn whether any of the men had been convicted of a violent crime. Finally, they pulled all the results together to answer the question of passionate interest to them: Could possession of the low-activity MAOA gene variant alchemize an abused child into a depraved adult?

It looked like the answer was yes.

Men with the low-activity gene version who had been maltreated turned out to be at a 10 times greater risk of committing a violent crime than those with the variant who had not been maltreated. Yet men with the high-activity version who had been maltreated were in no more danger of committing a violent crime than those with the high-activity version who had not been maltreated.

Furthermore, even though men who had both the low-activity gene and been mishandled constituted only 12 percent of the cohort, they had committed 44 percent of all the violent crimes committed by it! And 85 percent of the men who had both the low-activity gene and had been severely maltreated developed some form of antisocial behavior.

These provocative findings, reported in the August 2, 2002 *Science*, received lavish attention in the popular press. Moreover, some other scientists came up with similar results during the next few years.

Debra Foley, PhD, an assistant professor of human genetics at Virginia Commonwealth University, and colleagues reported in the July 2004 *Archives of General Psychiatry* that when the low-activity MAOA gene variant was combined with an adverse childhood environment, it elevated the prospect of youth engaging in conduct disorder.

"This is an important replication of the findings reported by Caspi *et al.* from this center in 2002," Peter McGuffin, MD, director of the Social, Genetic, and Developmental Psychiatry Center of the Institute of Psychiatry in London, told me. "...The fact that Foley *et al.* used a different methodology (for example, they used a simpler and retrospective measure of early adversity) and were studying a younger sample of subjects (here they looked at conduct disorder rather than adult antisocial disorder), but still found the same pattern as Caspi and colleagues suggests that the finding is robust."

Kent Nilsson, a PhD candidate at Uppsala University in Sweden, and his group interviewed 81 teens to learn whether they had ever engaged in antisocial acts, and if so, how often, and whether they had ever been physically, sexually, or emotionally mishandled either at home or in the neighborhood. After that, the scientists genotyped the boys to determine which ones had the low-activity or the high-activity MAOA gene variant and finally looked to see whether the boys with the former had engaged in markedly more antisocial acts than had the boys with the latter. The answer was yes only when the boys had an abuse background as well. These findings appeared in a 2005 *Biological Psychiatry*.

Then Julia Kim-Cohen, PhD, an assistant professor of psychology at Yale University, and her coworkers reported in the October 2006 *Molecular Psychiatry* that children who possessed the low-activity MAOA gene variant and had been physically abused exhibited more attention/deficit hyperactivity disorder symptoms, emotional problems, and antisocial behaviors than did children who had the high-activity variant and who had been physically abused.

So, the take-home message? When having the low-activity MAOA gene variant is coupled with childhood abuse, it can truly put youngsters in a dark place and lead them down the road to depravity. And as that tenet has come to be increasingly accepted by the scientific community, it is impacting society in some riveting ways.

Remember our friend James Fallon, whom we met at the start of this chapter, and how shocked he was to learn that his paternal ancestor gallery was packed with murderers? Shortly after, he started to worry that perhaps somebody in his immediate family had inherited a Fallon "mean gene." So he arranged to have 10 close relatives, plus himself, tested for the notorious low-activity MAOA gene variant.

As it turned out, only one of the 11 tested positive—himself! Once again, he was astonished. And disturbed. *Could I be a born killer?* Yet he had made it to 70 years of age without attacking or killing anybody. *So probably not,* he reasoned. But what had kept his malevolent low-activity MAOA gene variant from expressing itself? *Why, my terrific childhood!* he decided. It had been packed with attention and love from many quarters.

SOME OTHER GENE-ENVIRONMENT COMBOS CAN ALSO PROVE DEADLY

Unfortunately, the low-activity MAO gene variant plus abuse combo isn't the only one that can pave a path to evildoing. Some others have been identified as well, for example, the partnership between a virulent dopamine receptor gene variant and prenatal stress.

German researchers selected for their inquiry 308 pregnant women who had various reasons to feel stressed during pregnancy—little education, no spouse, family or obstetric problems—and evaluated them to determine actually how stressed they really felt. Three months after their children were born, the researchers determined whether the children possessed a variant of the dopamine receptor gene that had been linked with antisocial behaviors. The researchers followed the youngsters until they reached the age of 15, evaluated them for antisocial behaviors, and finally looked to see whether prenatal stress alone, or in combination with the noxious dopamine receptor gene variant, had any bearing on whether they engaged in antisocial behaviors or not.

Prenatal stress alone didn't, but prenatal stress plus the gene variant did, the researchers reported in the September 14, 2013 *Journal of Child Psychology and Psychiatry.*

So, which is more potent in pointing youth toward wrongdoing: genes or environment? I asked some of the experts on the subject this question.

"I think that there is evidence that the contribution of environment to delinquent behavior is larger than that of genetic factors," Frank Verhulst, MD, a child psychiatrist with Erasmus University in the Netherlands, told me.

A three-generation story from the American West seems to bolster his contention. A convicted Oregon killer named Ward Weaver Jr. sits on death row in San Quentin State Prison in California. His son, Ward Weaver III is also in prison for murder. As is his grandson, Francis Weaver. But here's the catch: Frank is not biologically related to either man; he was simply raised by the latter. Thus it looks as if it was Ward Weaver III's bad example, not genes, that prepped him for malfeasance.

Furthermore, whereas Ward Weaver Jr. buried one of his victims under a concrete slab in his backyard, his son Ward Weaver III did the same. The only difference is that he did his father one better and buried two victims, not just one, in this manner. Now, it's possible that mean genes son Ward inherited from father Ward had prompted him to imitate him, but it's much more likely, I think, that son Ward did what he did because he had observed father Ward's actions and wanted to imitate him.

However, S. Alexandra Burt, PhD, a Michigan State University researcher, doesn't agree with Verhulst that the environment has the upper hand over genes in the making of evildoers.

"Behavioral-genetics work to date suggests both," she said. "It is really a combination of the two."

Tanya Button, PhD, a postdoctoral fellow at the University of Colorado's Institute for Behavioral Genetics, concurs with Burt: "In studies of heritability, the proportion of the variance of antisocial behavior that can be attributed to genetic effects is 50 percent, and the other 50 percent is explained by environmental influences…Consequently, it is not possible to conclude that either genes or environment contribute more to antisocial behavior. Both are integral to its development."

Actually, "it is futile and silly to state either that genetic influences are stronger or that environmental factors are," evildoer expert Michael Stone, MD, maintains. "This is because the situation needs to be examined on a case-by-case basis."

In any event, coming from an abusive home seems to be the most *common* contributor to depravity, Stone noted, and it carries a compelling take-home message, he believes: "If you beat the heck out of your child, you're pushing him or her in the direction of becoming antisocial."

Indeed, two of the world's most infamous mass murderers, Hitler and Stalin, had fathers who savagely beat them, according to a documentary aired in December 2003 on *The History Channel*.

SIX

HOW THE BRAIN AND BODY
CAN CONTRIBUTE TO EVILDOING

Back in the late 19th Century, in the southeast corner of France, something incredibly gruesome happened: Thirteen shepherd boys were found butchered. The perpetrator was eventually identified: It was a man named Joseph Vacher. Vacher was also finally caught, unlike another serial killer busy at work in London around that time—Jack the Ripper.

Was Vacher mentally ill, which he claimed? The psychiatrists who examined him decided that he was not —rather, that he was rational and antisocial. Even as a youngster, they noted, he had been intelligent, but cruel.

Vacher was tried by a jury in 1898. The unanimous decision was that he was guilty without extenuating circumstances. He was sentenced to death and guillotined on the last day of 1898.

What had prompted Vacher to carry out all those ghastly killings? Was it because he had experienced a traumatic childhood? Maybe. One day, as a child, he had awakened to find that his twin, who was lying next to him, had been murdered. However, brain damage might have played a role instead. After his death, his brain was autopsied, and two bullets were found lodged in it.

Indeed, research conducted in recent years has underscored this latter hypothesis.

Evildoer expert Michael Stone, MD, (referred to in previous chapters) interviewed, or read in-depth biographies about, 145 serial killers. At least a fourth of them had experienced protracted periods of unconsciousness from head injury during childhood or early adolescence, he told me.

University of Pennsylvania researchers evaluated 113 female inmates convicted of either violent or nonviolent crimes. Ninety-five percent of all the inmates studied had incurred brain injuries preceding their crimes, but those who had committed violent acts, including murder, had experienced a greater number of such injuries.

THE PREFRONTAL CORTEX: A MAJOR SUSPECT

Moreover, advances in brain-imaging technology have provided still heftier evidence that brain afflictions can prep people for evildoing. They have also divulged that assaults on a particular brain area—the prefrontal cortex—can be especially pernicious in this regard. The front of your brain consists of a left frontal lobe and of a right frontal lobe, and at the tip of each frontal lobe can be found a prefrontal cortex. The prefrontal cortexes are located right above your eyes and behind your forehead. They are involved in judgment, planning, and decision-making.

A lot of the evidence linking the prefrontal cortex with wantonness has been obtained by an affable Brit-turned-American psychologist named Adrian Raine, PhD, whom I had the pleasure of meeting at a psychiatry conference a few years ago. After obtaining a bachelor's degree in psychology from Oxford University in 1977 and a doctorate in psychology from York University in 1982,

Raine worked as a prison psychologist at two top-security prisons in England. Subsequently, he became a lecturer in behavioral sciences at Nottingham University. He then immigrated to the United States in 1987 to become assistant professor of psychology at the University of Southern California. In 1994, he was named a full professor there.

In February 2000, Raine and his colleagues published study results in a highly respected psychiatric journal, *The Archives of General Psychiatry,* that garnered a fair amount of attention from the popular press. Using a brain-imaging technique called structural magnetic resonance imaging (structural MRI), they had found that the volume of prefrontal grey matter (nerve-cell bodies) was 11 percent less in 21 violent men, some of whom had committed murder, than in 21 controls—some with a history of drug and alcohol abuse and the others with no such history. These findings suggested that a paucity of prefrontal gray matter might contribute to violence and murder.

In a second study, Raine and his coworkers used a brain-imaging technique called positron emission tomography (PET) to evaluate glucose use in the prefrontal cortex of 41 murderers and of 41 controls – individuals who hadn't committed any crimes of violence. Brain cells use glucose as their fuel. The more active a brain region is, the more glucose it uses. The controls showed robust glucose use in the prefrontal cortex, the murderers a marked lack of it. This finding implied that a paucity of glucose use in the prefrontal cortex might contribute to violence and murder.

Back during your childhood, did you read the fairytale about the puppet Pinocchio? If so, you may recall that Pinocchio's nose grew longer with each lie he told. But what was going on in his head as he lied? The fairy tale didn't give us the answer. Yet Raine and company may well be able to do so, thanks to yet another investigation they conducted.

Raine and his team recruited subjects for this particular investigation by advertising at temporary-employment agencies. They didn't tell people interested in participating that it had to do with antisocial behavior, and especially with lying, since they also wanted to include a number of subjects who did not engage in such behaviors.

They ended up with 49 subjects—21 who had neither antisocial personality disorder nor a history of pathological lying; 16 with antisocial personality disorder, but no history of pathological lying, and 12 with a history of pathological lying only. None of the groups differed notably in social class, ethnicity, I.Q., handedness, history of head injury or some other factors that might have distorted results. Using structural MRI brain imaging, the researchers then evaluated not only the amount of gray matter (nerve cell bodies but the amount of white matter (nerve cell fibers) in the prefrontal cortexes of all 49 subjects. Nerve cell fibers, called axons, connect nerve cells and are covered by myelin (a type of fat). The myelin is what gives white matter its white color. Myelin speeds up signals between nerve cells, enabling them to quickly send and receive messages.

Compared with both antisocial and normal control subjects, the liars were found to have not just a 33 percent *reduction* in the ratio of prefrontal gray matter to prefrontal white matter, but a 25 percent *increase* in prefrontal white matter. "To our knowledge, this study is the first to show a brain abnormality in people who lie, cheat, and manipulate others," the scientists asserted in their study report, which was published in the October 2005 *British Journal of Psychiatry.*

The lead researcher, Yaling Yang, a doctoral student in brain science at the University of Southern California, did not expect these results, she told me in an interview. "I was surprised by how significantly different the brains of pathological liars and the brains of controls were," she said. "And I was surprised that the answer to pathological lying may be in white matter." To date, neuroscientists still focus more on gray matter than on white matter, she noted.

But how might a surplus of white matter in the prefrontal cortex unleash a torrent of untruths? Since white matter is pivotal to nerve connectivity and cognitive function, and since lying requires more work by the prefrontal cortex than telling the truth does, an excess of prefrontal white matter might confer a capacity for, or a predisposition to, lying, Sean Spence, MD, a professor of psychiatry at the University of Sheffield in England and a deception authority, speculated in an accompanying editorial.

MORE INDICTMENTS OF THE PREFRONTAL CORTEX

In any event, Raine and company are not the only scientists to have linked prefrontal cortex anomalies with foul behavior.

University of Connecticut researchers wanted to learn whether the brains of youth with conduct disorder respond differently to cognitive challenges than do the brains of youth without the disorder. They used a technique called event-related electroencephalographic potentials, where electrodes are placed all over the scalp, to achieve this aim in 158 teens. Half the teens had been diagnosed with conduct disorder, and half had not, thus serving as controls. The cognitive challenge the researchers decided to use was a memory task.

Whereas subjects without conduct problems showed a robust brain-wave response to the cognitive challenge in the prefrontal cortex, subjects with conduct problems did not. There were no marked differences between the two groups in other brain areas. So it looks as if an under-performing prefrontal cortex may contribute to conduct disorder.

Where in the depths of the human brain does antisocial violence have its inception? Investigators at the University of California at Los Angeles wanted to find out. They used structural MRI to measure the thickness of various brain areas in four starkly different groups – 14 individuals with antisocial personality disorder and a history of violence; 12 individuals with schizophrenia and a history of violence; 15 individuals with schizophrenia, but no history of violence, and 15 mentally healthy nonviolent comparison subjects.

Only one thing separated the violent antisocial group from the other three – an extremely thin prefrontal cortex. But if an extremely thin prefrontal cortex contributes to violence, then how does it actually do it? By failing to put the brakes on hateful impulses, the scientists proposed in their paper, which appeared in the September 2007 *American Journal of Psychiatry*. After all, the prefrontal cortex is critical to judgment, decision-making, and self-control. It's the part of your brain that makes you think twice before doing anything.

Although scientists don't give much weight to anecdotal reports, in contrast to case-control studies or brain-imaging studies, for example, there is one that appears to bolster the argument that prefrontal cortex defects contribute to evildoing and that deserves mention. While performing an operation to remove a patient's nasal polyps, a doctor inadvertently damaged the patient's prefrontal cortex. In the months that followed, the patient developed symptoms of antisocial behavior. She eventually murdered her mother.

Nonetheless, the prefrontal cortex isn't the only area in the front part of the brain that scientists are implicating in bad behavior.

A lack of empathy is one of the hallmarks of psychopathic individuals. What area or areas of their brains cause or contribute to this deficit? University of Chicago scientists wanted to find out. They selected for their study 80 prison inmates, some who were psychopaths and some who were not, and exposed them to photos of people in pain or distress. Meanwhile, the researchers tracked the function of the inmates' brains with a brain- imaging technique called functional magnetic resonance imaging (fMRI), then compared the results for the psychopathic and non-psychopathic groups. Compared to controls, the psychopaths showed much less response to the stimulus not just in the prefrontal cortex, but in the orbitofrontal cortex. The orbitofrontal cortex, like the prefrontal cortex, is part of the frontal lobe. And since a person has two frontal lobes, that means that he has not only two prefrontal cortexes, but two orbitofrontal cortexes. And if both prefrontal cortexes and both orbitofrontal cortexes are malfunctioning, one can imagine that that quadruple insult could well erode his capacity for empathy.

SUPPOSE SOMEONE YOU LOVE STARTED ACTING CREEPY?

But wait: Even more cerebral villains may contribute to base behavior. Here are some weird but true stories,

Forty-five-year-old "Kyle" started showing personality changes that baffled and disturbed his wife, teenage sons, and colleagues at work. He became sloppy in his dress, showed a lack of compassion for people, made lewd remarks, and attempted to grab the buttocks of a female co-worker.

A fifty-two-year-old, "Laura," also incurred personality changes that alarmed those who knew and cared about her. She expressed sadness over the death of a relative, then burst into laughter. She started stealing items in stores even when she knew the owners. Only the intervention of her family kept the owners from prosecuting her.

"Will," a 57-year-old, had always been a loving son and husband. Yet he did not show any sadness when his mother died; nor did he visit his wife while she was hospitalized. After he rear-ended a car, he raced from the scene without any concern for the man he had hit. He also laughed inappropriately, made embarrassing comments, and started belching and passing gas in the presence of others.

"Rusty," a well-heeled 63-year-old, likewise started showing signs of disinhibition and a lack of concern for others. He stopped showering and wore the same clothes every day. He burst into offices at work and interrupted conversations. He started stalking and attempting to molest children. When he exposed himself to the children next door, he was arrested.

Kyle, Laura, Will, and Rusty were required to undergo extensive neurological and psychiatric evaluations, including brain imaging, in hopes of explaining their strange and vexing behaviors.

Three out of four of them showed abnormally low glucose metabolism in the temporal lobes. There are two temporal lobes in the human brain, one on each side. One of them also showed abnormally low glucose metabolism in the prefrontal cortexes of the frontal lobes as well. These findings, plus others, suggested that all four were all coming down with a form of dementia called frontotemporal dementia, which especially impacts the frontal lobes and the temporal lobes of the brain, and which can cause emotional blunting, socially inappropriate behavior, and a lack of empathy.

These four case histories, published in the July 2010 *Journal of the American Academy of Psychiatry and the Law*, also suggest, I contend, that even if people don't have frontotemporal dementia, damage to their temporal lobes, just like damage to their frontal lobes, might possibly prime them for wanton behavior.

And there is ample science to back my hunch.

Scientists at the Institute of Psychiatry, King's College London recruited 17 antisocial and psychopathic violent offenders; 27 antisocial, but non-psychopathic violent offenders; and 22 non-offenders (controls) for a study. The researchers used structural MRI to measure the brain volumes of the three groups of subjects, then compared the results.

There were no notable differences between the antisocial-with-out-psychopathy group and the controls, which surprised them, they admitted in their paper, which appeared online in the *Archives of General Psychiatry* on May 7, 2012. But they *did* find striking difference in the antisocial-with-psychopathy group compared to both the antisocial-without-psychopathy group and the controls. It was reduced gray matter not just in the prefrontal cortexes of the frontal lobes, but in the poles of the temporal lobes, suggesting that reduced gray matter in both brain regions might contribute to psychopathy.

Especially Concerning: Faulty Alarm Centers

Furthermore, there is reason to suspect that an almond-shape cluster of neurons tucked away in the dark labyrinth of each temporal lobe may play a role in psychopathy. This is the amygdala. The amygdalae are the brain's alarm centers, igniting some of our worst fears and anxieties. One sign that the amygdalae have been activated is the startle reflex. Can you recall awaiting an important phone call and jumping when the phone rang? That's your amygdalae going off.

Worry warts have highly active amygdalae. A noise might make them jump out of their seats. I happen to be one of those. People with more temperate amygdalae might notice the noise, but not be particularly bothered by it. And then there are those individuals who have very sluggish amygdalae; they tend to keep their cool when they hear a noise or are otherwise stressed. Although some individuals with sluggish amygdalae are undoubtedly exemplary citizens, using their under-performing amygdalae in their work—one can imagine, for instance, many firefighters, police, or brain surgeons falling in this group—others are certainly not exemplary. The reasons? Amygdala under-responsiveness has been identified not just in adult criminals, bur in youth with conduct disorder, and even in university students scoring high on psychopathic traits such as egocentricity, irresponsibility, pathological lying, manipulativeness, a lack of empathy, a lack of guilt, and a lack of remorse.

One of the most intriguing studies implicating amygdala abnormalities in depravity was published May 6, 2013 in *Biological Psychiatry*.

It all started in 1987 when two University of Pittsburgh researchers, Rolf Loeber, PhD, and Magda Stouthamer-Loeber, PhD, launched the Pittsburgh Youth Study. This was a longitudinal study of some 500 inner-city boys, meaning the researchers examined and re-examined the same individuals, recording any changes that occurred over time. The goal of this study was to document the development of antisocial and delinquent behavior from childhood to early adulthood. A scientist named Dustin Pardini, PhD, joined the research team in 2004. Kirk Erickson, PhD joined after that.

Around 2007, Rolf Loeber, Pardini, and Erickson teamed up with that veteran at peering into the brains of the depraved, Adrian Raine, PhD, to use the Pittsburgh Youth Study for a new investigation. (At this juncture, Raine was no longer affiliated with the University of Southern California, but had become a professor of criminology, psychiatry, and psychology at the University of Pennsylvania.)

They recruited 56 men who had participated in the Pittsburgh Youth Study up to age 26 and whose levels of aggression and psychopathic features during childhood, adolescence, and early adulthood had been measured. According to self-assessment and criminal records, 20 had a history of chronic serious violence, 16 a history of transient serious violence, and 20 a history of no serious violence.

The researchers used structural MRI imaging to measure the amygdalae of the 56 subjects. The researchers then looked to see whether there was any link between the size of the subjects' amygdalae and the amount of aggression and psychopathy the subjects had shown back in childhood and adolescence, taking potential confounds such as age, handedness, concussions, and childhood maltreatment into consideration. The answer was yes. Subjects with smaller amygdalae had exhibited markedly more aggression and psychopathic features in childhood and adolescence than had those subjects with larger amygdalae.

Now, this finding strongly suggests that puny amygdalae might have led the subjects to engage in aggression and psychopathy. But a subsequent chapter in this investigation is even more convincing, I think.

The scientists followed the same subjects for three more years, then evaluated them for aggression and psychopathy at that time. After that, they looked to see whether there was any link between the size of the subjects' amygdalae three years earlier and their subsequent levels of aggression and psychopathy.

Indeed there was: Those with smaller amygdalae were three times more likely than those with larger ones to exhibit aggression and psychopathy three years later.

"This was somewhat surprising given that it is particularly difficult to determine who will continue to engage in violent behavior over time," Pardini told me in 2013.

WHEN THE BRAIN'S REWARD CENTER BACKFIRES

Finally, a cluster of neurons located in neither the frontal lobe nor the temporal lobe of each brain hemisphere, but close to the former may possibly also set people up for nasty behavior. This is the nucleus accumbens, the brain's reward center. If you feel good after listening to music, exercising, drinking a cocktail, or having sex, you can thank the nucleus accumbens in each of your two brain hemispheres for those feel-good feelings.

However, the nuclei accumbens don't always lead to bliss.

Joshua Buckholtz, a doctoral candidate in neuroscience at Vanderbilt University, and colleagues suspected that there might be a link between impulsive antisociality and the nucleus accumbens. They launched a study to find out.

They recruited 24 community volunteers and evaluated each of them to see how they rated on impulsive antisociality. Impulsive antisociality in turn has been associated with antisocial behavior, aggression, impulsivity, and substance abuse in both prison and community samples.

In a first experiment, the subjects were given an amphetamine, which is known to increase levels of the nerve transmitter dopamine in the nucleus accumbens. After that, PET scans were used to measure the amount of dopamine released in the nuclei accumbens of each subject. The researchers looked to see whether there was any correlation between how high subjects had scored on impulsive antisociality and the amount of dopamine released.

Indeed, there was. The higher subjects had scored on impulsive antisociality, the more dopamine they released. In fact, when the highest-scoring subjects were compared with the lowest-scoring ones, the former released four times more dopamine than the latter did.

In a second experiment, the subjects played a game in which they could win a cash reward. While they were playing the game, fMRI scans were used to see how much dopamine was released in their nuclei accumbens. The higher subjects had scored on impulsive antisociality, the more dopamine they released.

Thus, combining results from both experiments, it looks as if people who are impulsively antisocial possess especially responsive nuclei accumbens.

But what do these findings mean in practical terms? One

possibility is that people with overly active nuclei accumbens might be aggressive about obtaining whatever they consider rewarding, whether it is drugs, sex, money, or something else. Rodent studies have shown that dopamine is released from the nucleus accumbens during aggressive behavior, and aggressive behavior is common among antisocial or psychopathic individuals.

THE BAD GUYS AREN'T ALL IN THE BRAIN

So, all things considered, wickedness can probably not be blamed solely on irregularities in any one brain area Nor can it be blamed only on culprits above the neck.

Sit down in a comfortable chair, then grasp a blood vessel on each side of your neck. Can you feel blood from your heart coursing through one of the vessels?

Now, while pressing on the pulse, count the number of throbs you feel during 15 seconds—let's say it's 16 beats— and multiply that number by four. You end up with 16 times four, or 64. That's your pulse, or resting heart rate. Your pulse can tell some intriguing things about you.

A normal resting heart rate is between 60 and 100 beats per minute (bpm), depending on a person's age and physical condition. A lower rate may indicate more efficient heart function and fitness. A highly trained athlete may have a resting heart rate closer to 40 bpm.

A lower rate may also indicate a talent for staying cool under duress. Some individuals who have this talent use it to undertake dangerous missions in order to benefit society. For instance, bomb-disposal experts and decorated paratroopers have been found to have markedly low resting heart rates while out in the field. In contrast, other individuals who have low rates and who are able to stay cool under duress use their talent to harm others.

Actually, it would be hard to dispute that there is a potent link between a low resting heart rate and antisocial behavior. The finding has been replicated in geographic areas as far flung as England, the United States, Germany, Siberia, New Zealand, and Mauritius (an island country in the southwest Indian Ocean). The link does not appear to be an artifact of potentially confounding factors such as height, weight, body build, physical fitness, social class, or psychosocial adversity. Moreover, it can be found in youth as well as in adults, in girls as well as in boys, and is even a strong predictor of future antisocial behavior.

SEROTONIN: ANOTHER BRAIN–BODY FACTOR TO CONSIDER

Nonetheless, a low heart rate is not the only brain-body constituent that may be capable of setting people up for egregious behavior. Another strong contender is low levels of the feel-good nerve transmitter serotonin.

Low levels of serotonin in the brain are well known to cause depression; many antidepressants work by upping these levels. But low levels of serotonin in the brain may also be capable of unleashing impulsive aggression.

Now true, researchers are unable to measure the amount of serotonin in the human brain directly, but they are able to do so indirectly by measuring the amount of serotonin and its metabolites (breakdown products) in cerebrospinal fluid, which courses from the brain down along the spinal cord. Thus, if they detect a paucity of serotonin or its metabolites in cerebrospinal fluid, they are able to deduce that there's a scarcity of these chemicals in the brain as well.

Using this indirect method of measurement, scientists have linked low levels of serotonin or its metabolites with impulsively aggressive behaviors in a variety of settings.

For example, low levels of serotonin or its metabolites have been

found in the cerebrospinal fluid of individuals who have died by suicide or have tried to kill themselves, in prison inmates who have murdered, in youth who have killed pet animals in a rage, in youth who
have set fires impulsively, and even in some temper-prone individuals.

However, a paucity of serotonin in brain and body may not
contribute to depravity that has been thought out ahead of time. The
reason is this. A drug known to ramp up levels of serotonin was given
to some prisoners who had committed either impulsive murders or
premeditated murders. The drug cooled aggression in the former, but
not the latter, suggesting that serotonin and its metabolites play no
role in premeditated aggression.

TESTOSTERONE: ANOTHER POSSIBLE CULPRIT WITH SURPRISING TWISTS

Throughout the years, whenever a young male driver would
honk behind us, or zip past our car and give us the finger, I would
comment to my husband: "There goes another young guy with too
much testosterone!"

Although women have a little of the male sex hormone testosterone in their bodies, men have a lot more of it, and especially young
men in their prime. Moreover, high levels of testosterone have been
linked with aggression in both male animals and in human males. But
does that mean that testosterone can not only turn men into offensive
louts, but into serious criminals?

Maybe. In one study of 692 inmates, those with high testosterone levels were more likely to commit violent crimes and violate
prison rules than those with lower testosterone levels.

Or maybe not. In another study, researchers measured the
levels of testosterone in the blood of prison inmates and also gave
the inmates psychological tests measuring aggression and antisocial
traits. The researchers could find no relationship between high levels

of testosterone and high aggression and high antisocial scores. But they *did* find a link between a chemical that binds to testosterone in the blood and high aggression and high antisocial scores. The chemical is called sex hormone-binding globulin, and it in turn is linked to alcohol or drug abuse. So, it's possible that this chemical, rather than testosterone, can pressure men into doing nasty things.

But how about testosterone and male sex offending? Surely testosterone must be a major culprit since it is a potent male sex hormone? Once again, you may be in for a surprise.

One of Canada's leading sex-offender experts, psychiatrist John Bradford, MD, and his team decided to conduct a longitudinal study to see whether testosterone contributes to sex offending. Their cohort consisted of almost 800 men who had been convicted of child sexual abuse, exhibitionism, adult rape, or other sexual offenses, and who had been evaluated at the time of conviction for blood levels of not just testosterone, but of luteinizing hormone (LH) and follicle-stimulating hormone (FSH). LH and FSH—which are also referred to as gonadotrophic hormones—are made by the pituitary gland in the brain. LH stimulates a man's testes to produce testosterone; FSH stimulates a man's testes to make sperm.

Each offender was once again living in the community, although being watched by the police for any further sexual offense. While some offenders had been observed for as long as 20 years, the average length of observation was 11 years.

Bradford and his team examined a national database maintained by the Royal Canadian Mounted Police to see whether any of the offenders had re-offended since returning to the community. They found that 18 percent had. They then looked to see whether there were any links between re-offenders' initial testosterone, LH, and FSH levels and their later recidivism. The answer was "no" as far as testosterone was concerned, but "yes" as far as LH and FSH levels were.

"This study is an important one, with a surprising finding that gonadotrophic hormones were better predictors of recidivism for sexual crimes than testosterone," Richard Krueger, MD, an associate clinical professor of psychiatry at Columbia University and one of America's leading sex-offender experts, told me. The reason why it's so unexpected, he said, is because testosterone plays such a prominent role in sexual function and in sexual and nonsexual aggression.

So, if LH and FSH are more complicit in sexual offending than testosterone is, then how do they go about it? Alas, we'll have to wait until scientists can provide us with the answers.

CAN EVILDOING CONTRIBUTORS WORK IN CONCERT?

Meanwhile, let's try to pull all of this material together. Prefrontal cortex deficits, amygdala deficits, a sluggish heart rate, a paucity of serotonin, as well as other physiological factors, can undoubtedly contribute to heinous behavior. But so can mean genes and a toxic environment. So the question now is: Can any of these noxious actors conspire together to promote depravity?

It looks as though they can.

Throughout the years, New York City psychiatrist Dorothy Lewis, MD, had occasion to evaluate six young men whose lives seemed to have encompassed one tragedy after another. Each had had at least one biological parent with a serious psychiatric illness. In two of the men's families, severe mental illness could be traced back even two generations, and in one of the men's families, even three. Each had experienced obstetric complications during birth or a brain injury afterward. Each was adopted by parents who abused or even abandoned him. And most chilling of all, each ended up with serious psychiatric illness himself and ultimately murdered someone.

One shot two security guards who stopped him as he raced around in a stolen speed boat. A second stabbed a female neighbor to death, then raped and sodomized her with a metal pole. A third shot and killed a meter maid over a dispute about a parking ticket. A fourth raped, sodomized, and murdered two women. A fifth stabbed an older woman who had come to collect a debt. And the sixth shot his adoptive parents to death.

What made these young men do such despicable things? Bad genes? Brain damage during or after birth? A toxic childhood environment? Or perhaps all of these ingredients? We will never know for sure, but probably it was a combination. That, in any event, was Lewis's opinion. "There was no evidence of a specific 'bad seed' for violence," she tells us." [It was the] adoptees' intrinsic vulnerabilities to psychoses and to the impulsiveness and emotional lability often associated with early brain trauma, coupled with maltreatment, [that] predisposed them to homicidal violence."

A similar situation seems to exist regarding serial killers. There is not just one contributor. As mentioned earlier, at least a fourth of the serial killers evildoer expert Michael Stone, MD, studied had experienced severe brain injuries in childhood or adolescence, suggesting that the injuries triggered their base behavior. Yet many other serial killers in Stone's cohort had experienced atrocious childhoods, implying that their childhoods had prompted them to engage in horrific acts. And still others had experienced neither. In these instances, the origin of their behaviors may have been brain damage induced by obstetric complications during birth or perhaps a genetic predisposition to psychopathy as measured in a low heart rate.

But in the vast majority of cases, the killers' appalling acts had probably been unleashed by more than one contributor because, as Stone told me, "Of all the risk factors that researchers have identified in people who become violently aggressive, many were present in many of these men."

Nonetheless, out of the raft of factors that may be capable of grooming people to commit dastardly deeds, I can't help but suspect that one of them must surely be the most pernicious. Until scientists can give us an answer to this question, I'm going to place my bet on an abusive childhood. Here's why.

First off, even though Stone was unable to tell me which pre-disposing factor was the most critical in alchemizing the men in his cohort into serial killers, he *did* tell me that a traumatic childhood was the most common.

And then there was a study where scientists used Sweden's large and extensive databases about its citizens to determine whether obstetric complications or inadequate or inappropriate parenting are risk factors for later criminal behavior. The answer turned out to be "No" for obstetric complications, but a resounding "Yes" for inadequate or inappropriate parenting. And in those few cases where subjects had been the victims of both obstetric complications *and* inadequate or inappropriate parenting, their risk of later criminal behavior was only slightly more than if they had experienced inadequate or inappropriate parenting alone.

SEVEN
HOW ABOUT FREE WILL?

The city of Louisville, Kentucky is situated on the banks of the Ohio River, across from Indiana. It is famous for fast horses, beautiful women, and mint juleps – the Kentucky Derby. The inventor of Kentucky Fried Chicken, Colonel Sanders, is buried in Louisville's Cave Hill Cemetery. So is heavyweight boxing champion Muhammad Ali.

But on September 14, 1989, Louisville made headlines for less felicitous reasons. A man named Joseph Wesbecker walked into the printing plant of *The Louisville Courier-Journal* and shot 20 people, eight of whom died, before he committed suicide.

Wesbecker, it happened, had been taking the antidepressant Prosac before he engaged in these deadly acts. Consequently, lawyers representing the families of the victims sued Eli Lilly and Company, the maker of Prosac, claiming that "Prosac had made him do it."

The jury didn't buy this argument. But it does raise a similar question as far as evildoing is concerned: Could specific genes, specific environmental experiences, or certain brain or biological quirks *make* a person commit dark and grisly deeds?

Actually, a lot of evidence can be rallied to argue that they could. For instance, as we learned in the previous two chapters, a number of gene variants; a welter of adverse childhood experiences; and various types of brain defects plus some other biological anomalies have been linked with depraved behaviors. And suppose that a person has not just one, or two, but a number of such risk factors? Wouldn't his (or her) evildoing destiny be a done deal? It sounds as if might be from a comment evildoer expert Michael Stone, MD, shared with me.

"Of all the factors that researchers have lately identified in people who become violently aggressive, many are present in many serial killers. So, if you come from a broken home, and you are beaten by your folks, and you have a head injury, and, and, and – in other words, you have a multiplicity of these risk factors," you may well end up engaging in premeditated types of aggression such as serial killing.

Still another compelling reason to believe that noxious nature and nurture factors inevitably lead to base behaviors comes from the four individuals introduced in the previous chapter who were coming down with a form of dementia called frontotemporal dementia. As this form of dementia started to destroy various parts of their brains, notably the ventromedial (bottom-middle) part of their prefrontal cortexes, they started to engage in deleterious behaviors, such as shoplifting, exposing, inappropriate touching, or making lewd comments.

Since the ventromedial part of the prefrontal cortex is known to be crucial for the emotions of compassion, shame, guilt, and regret, one could argue that dementia damage to this part of the brain *made* them engage in such behaviors. A still more striking reason to believe that this was the case is this: All four of the individuals said that they had known what they were doing was wrong and harmful yet did not feel the need to restrain from doing it. So, did their ventromedial prefrontal cortexes *make* them do it? One could certainly argue that this was the case.

STILL, A CASE CAN BE MADE FOR FREE WILL

One of the most astonishing, and baffling, aspects of the story about serial killer-cannibal Jeffrey Dahmer concerns his father Lionel. When Lionel was a youth, he would awaken at times feeling as if he had committed murder. That is one reason why Lionel feared that he might have passed on one or more "killer genes" to his son. Yet unlike his son, Lionel did not act on his dark dreams and impulses. Was it perhaps because Lionel *chose to not act on them?* No one knows. In any event, ample evidence can be rallied to support the premise that an adverse biology and an adverse childhood *do not necessarily lead* to wicked behavior.

Let's first go back in time to a Swedish child psychiatric pioneer named Alice Hellstrom, MD. She founded a school-home for "psychopathic" children in 1928. These were youngsters who came from the wrong side of the tracks. They had criminal or alcoholic parents. They were doing bad things. They were obviously headed for a dissolute future.

Hellstrom not only worked to improve their lives but tracked their outcomes as the years went by. After she died, some other researchers continued the task, so that eventually detailed information was available for 242 children who had attended the school-home between 1928 and 1940. The researchers analyzed the data to see what had become of them.

Despite Hellstrom's efforts to improve the youngsters' lives, 45 percent of the boys and 11 percent of the girls still ended up becoming criminals and/or alcoholics. But here's the silver lining: The remaining 55 percent of the boys and the remaining 89 percent of the girls did not. Had Hellstrom's efforts made a difference as far as the latter group was concerned? This was quite possible. And it was also feasible that some, or perhaps many, of the latter group *had decided not to pursue a decadent life.*

Let's move on to England and focus on the subject of low physiological arousal—things such as a low heart rate and a low perspiration rate in face of a stressful situation. As you may recall from the last chapter, such low arousal has been linked with antisocial behaviors, probably because it's necessary to keep your cool if you're going to hold somebody up or rob a bank. Indeed, in one English study, schoolboys were measured for physiological arousal, then followed up for nine years until they were 24 years of age to see whether those with low arousal measures were more likely to pursue a life of crime. Not surprisingly, the answer was yes. But it's not just criminals who have low physiological arousal, another English study found: Bomb-disposal experts do as well. The question is: Why do some people with low physiological arousal pursue a life of crime, and even murder, whereas others with low physiological arousal pursue a life of saving people? *Could choice perhaps have something to do with it?*

And now, let's hop across the *Big Pond* to the United States. As we learned in the previous chapter, some researchers at the University of Southern California were keen on identifying brain areas involved in pathological lying. The lead researcher was doctoral student Yaling Yang. Adrian Raine, PhD, an expert on what transpires in the brains of criminals, was also part of the team.

Pathological liars con, deceive, malinger; they are, in essence, psychopaths. The study as noted in Chapter 6 included 49 subjects:21 normal subjects, —who had neither antisocial personality disorder nor a history of pathological lying; 16 subjects with antisocial personality disorder, but no history of pathological lying; and 12 subjects with a history of pathological lying. The researchers performed brain scans on the three groups of subjects, then compared the results. In contrast to both normal and antisocial subjects, the pathological liars had dramatically more white matter in their prefrontal cortexes.

Yang was surprised by this finding, he told me, since neuroscientists have traditionally been much more interested in the brain's gray matter (nerve-cell bodies), than in the brain's white matter (nerve-cell fibers). In any event, one could argue that this finding shows that an excess of white matter in the prefrontal cortex *makes* a person lie. Or you could posit, as has Sean Spence, MD, a deception authority at the University of Sheffield in England, that lying increases the amount of white matter in the prefrontal cortex. And if this is the case, then anatomy does not drive deception, but deception drives anatomy, and lying may well be something you *choose* to do.

Some perspective offered by New York City forensic psychiatrists Paul Appelbaum, MD and Michael Stone, MD also appears to bolster the argument that turpitude involves choice.

Even though many studies have found statistically significant links between various risk factors and antisocial behaviors, all that it means is that the links exist beyond chance – not that the risk factors necessarily *cause* the behaviors, Appelbaum warns us.

Researchers have found that the more evildoing risk factors youth possess, the more likely they may be to become evildoers. "Even where many risk factors are present at once, however, we are far from being able to claim real causal inevitability for this or that combination of such factors," Stone cautions. "This is because people can usually be found who have never violated social norms, yet who are burdened with similar combinations of adverse nature and nurture factors."

SO, DO NATURE AND NURTURE DRIVE DESTINY OR NOT?

Nonetheless, evildoing authorities do have their opinions on the subject.

"Neuroscience is confirming what psychiatrists have always

known, that total free will is a fiction," ventures Georgetown University psychiatrist Robert I. Simon, MD. "...When psychiatrists examine the individual and the circumstances, they may discover that free will played a minor role or no role in the individual's choices and actions."

"...Just because our brains may be hard-wired for basic emotions like rage, does this mean that we have little or no control over them?" New York City psychiatrist Richard A. Friedman, MD, asks us. "In a word, no," he replies. "With the small exception of those people with actual brain injury who literally lack the requisite neural hardware to control their emotional impulses, the rest of us can be expected to weather the storm of our emotions without acting on them."

As Ervin Staub, PhD, a Massachusetts psychologist and Holocaust survivor, has written: "All that I have learned in the course of my studies of children and adults; my work with teachers and parents; my study of genocide and mass killing; my engagement in real-life situations like Rwanda; trying to help prevent renewed violence after the genocide of 1994 by promoting healing and reconciliation; my work with police officers and others; and my study of others' work tells me that human beings have the potential for both goodness and evil..."

"Contemporary psychiatrists and psychologists do not have an answer to the free will problem any more than do philosophers," avows Minnesota psychiatrist Carl Malmquist, MD. "The most that can be argued is that certain types of mental disorders impinge on the degree of freedom a person has about choosing between options. To conclude that a person has no choice in violent acts, and that he or she had to kill someone, is an undemonstratable position."

"Alcoholics know they have a problem, that their biological and genetic predisposition makes them more likely to drink," Adrian

Raine, PhD, states. "So they have the responsibility to seek help... You could say the same is true of these violent criminal offenders [with abnormal prefrontal cortexes]—they know they have these risk factors, and that they ought to do something about it. That's fine, but the part of the brain that's responsible for self-reflection and insight is the prefrontal cortex. And it's damaged. [So] it's a double-whammy ...[On the other hand,] there are people who commit violent crimes who have none of the predispositions. I do believe [that they have] freedom of will. I do believe that people can of their own free will choose an evil path in life."

In the opinion of Charles Murray, PhD, coauthor of the *Bell Curve*, a highly controversial book about I.Q. in American society, if one gene influences one behavior, then other genes probably influence others, and these various influences undoubtedly interplay and perhaps even contradict each other. And if that is the case, it should disabuse us from the illusion that people's behaviors are totally controlled by their genes.

And let's hear from Sally Satel, MD, a Washington, DC psychiatrist and author of various magazine articles and popular books. Satel admits to being a true believer in free will. She holds that it exists even in addicts, where people's values, desires, and motivations come to bear on their choices. And while she has "incredible respect and admiration" for brain-imaging technology and finds "the seduction of brain images astounding," she does not believe that brain activity visualized with neuroimaging dictates what a person does. Nor does she believe that other advances in neuroscience besides brain imaging are ever going to disprove free will.

THE MAOA GENE GOES ON TRIAL

Meanwhile, criminal defense lawyers are tapping the ever-growing arsenal of documented evildoing risk factors to get their clients off.

For instance, when Susan Smith went on trial in 1995 for drowning her children, her lawyers used evidence that she was depressed and that suicide attempts ran in her family as part of her defense.

Some defense lawyers have argued that their clients engaged in acts of impulsive violence because their brain levels of the neurotransmitter serotonin were low. This "Serotonin made me do it" argument was based on studies that have found a statistically significant link between low levels of serotonin and violence.

"We are seeing a growing introduction of both structural and functional neuroimages, electrophysiological studies, and genetic information in court in connection with a variety of claims," Appelbaum told me.

Forensic psychiatrist William Bernet, MD, a professor emeritus at Vanderbilt University, concurred. "The brain-imaging movement in forensic psychiatry in recent years is a reflection of the push in all of psychiatry, and with the completion of the human genome project [in 2002], there has been a lot of interest in genetic testing in forensic situations."

So how are such defenses playing out?

Sometimes they flop; other times they work.

For example, in 1995, a 20-year-old named Christopher Beck killed his cousin and her two housemates in Arlington, Virginia. In 1996, he was tried, found guilty and given three death sentences. In 2001, shortly before he was scheduled to be executed, his attorneys attempted to save his life by filing a clemency petition. In the petition, they pointed out that Beck had had a traumatic childhood—his mother had abused alcohol and drugs, his father had hung himself, and Beck had been sexually assaulted at age seven. The US Supreme Court refused to halt the execution.

But then there was the case of Bradley Waldroup, who lived in a trailer in the mountains of Tennessee. On October 16, 2006, Waldroup's wife Penny came to his trailer with a girlfriend to tell him that she was leaving him. In a rage, Waldroup shot the girlfriend eight times and sliced her head open with a sharp object. He then chased after Penny with a machete, chopping off her finger and cutting her over and over.

Prosecutors charged Waldroup with the felony murder of the girlfriend, which carried the death penalty, and attempted first-degree murder of Penny. Waldroup's defense lawyer, Wylie Richardson, went to forensic psychiatrist William Bernet, MD, quoted above, and asked whether he would evaluate Waldroup psychiatrically. Bernet not only did that but tested Waldroup for the infamous low-activity MAOA gene variant. As it turned out, Waldroup had not only a history of child abuse, but the gene variant. Richardson wanted Bernet to introduce these findings in court as part of Waldroup's defense. Despite fierce opposition from the prosecutors, the judge allowed it.

After 11 hours of deliberation, the jury convicted Waldroup of voluntary manslaughter—not murder—and attempted second-degree murder. One of the jurors admitted afterward that the science had helped persuade her that Waldroup had not been entirely in control of his actions. "A bad gene is a bad gene," she said.

The prosecutors, Drew Richardson and Cynthia Lecroy-Schemel, were stunned by the outcome. "I was just flabbergasted," Richardson said. "I did not know how to react to it."

"Anything that defense attorneys can ... latch onto to save their client's life or to lessen their client's culpability, they will do it," Lecroy-Schemel lamented.

Park Dietz, MD, PhD, a Newport Beach, California forensic psychiatrist who has testified in some high-profile criminal cases, is also unhappy about this state of affairs. "Hard data from brain imaging and genetic studies aren't sufficiently mature for the courtroom yet and serve mostly to mislead jurors into adopting overly deterministic concepts of criminal behavior," he told me. For example, let's say a defendant has a gene variant known to increase the odds of doing something terrible tenfold. "All that really means is that the defendant's biology raised his odds of killing from five in 100,000 to five in 10,000. Does that mean that he had no choice?"

Nonetheless, evildoing risk factors will undoubtedly continue to be incorporated into criminal defenses. Deborah Denno, PhD, JD, a professor of law at Fordham University, studied 81 criminal cases fro, 1994, when forensic psychiatry became an official subspecialty, up to 2011, to see how often judges admitted psychiatric genetic evidence into court proceedings. The evidence could have been, for example, that mental illness was prevalent in a defendant's family or that a defendant had a genetic propensity toward alcoholism or substance abuse. During this 17-year period, judges became increasingly accepting of such evidence, she found.

EIGHT
EVILDOERS: SOME DEMOGRAPHIC PERSPECTIVE

MEN ARE FAR MORE LIKELY THAN WOMEN TO COMMIT WANTON ACTS.

Does that sound like a sexist claim? Probably. Yet there is hefty evidence to support it.

Ninety-five percent of child abductor-sexual abusers, 90 percent of murderers, 87 percent of stalkers, and 83 percent of serial killers are men. Depending on the study, anywhere between two and eight times more men than women have antisocial personality disorder. There are six times more male psychopaths than there are female psychopaths, and psychopaths in turn commit over half of all violent crimes. Most arsonists, exhibitionists, and sadists are men. The list goes on. In brief, males are far more likely to commit vile acts than females are, evildoer expert Michael Stone, MD, reports.

There are several explanations for this state of affairs.

Men tend to be physically stronger than women.

Men are apt to be more aggressive and violent than women. One reason why is hormonal. Men are apt to have much more of the sex hormone testosterone in their bodies than women do, and testosterone in turn has been linked with both sexual and non-sexual aggression. Another reason why may be because men are more prone to taking risks than women are. And still a third: When faced with stressors, men are more likely to use outward aggression to cope, whereas women are more likely to use inward coping strategies such as becoming depressed, feeling guilty, or abusing substances.

Finally, men are more likely to take a relaxed stance toward morally questionable acts than are women, evildoer expert Michael Welner, MD, found during his Depravity Scale research.

Nonetheless, women sometimes match men in depravity. This sometimes occurs when they have been exposed to extremely stressful life situations, such as physical or sexual abuse. This sometimes occurs when they have a serious mental illness. "Men and women with serious mental illness are about equally likely to be involved in violent behavior," Jeffrey Swanson, PhD, an associate professor of psychiatry at Duke University, told me. "But with men, it is more likely to happen against people they don't know very well, whereas with women, it is more likely to occur in the home."

Here are a few examples of women doing some pretty vile things…

In December 2001, in an isolated farmhouse near Leesburg, Virginia, a gene researcher named Robert Schwartz was found stabbed to death. A youth named Kyle Hulbert was the apparent perpetrator. However, online chats retrieved from the computer belonging to Schwartz's daughter, Clara Jane Schwartz, suggested that she had been the one to plot the murder and to persuade Hulbert to carry it out. Clara was arrested on February 1, 2002 and charged with first-degree murder. On October 16, 2002, a jury convicted her of first-degree murder, and on February 10, 2003, she was sentenced to 48 years in prison. She is currently imprisoned in a correctional facility in Troy, Virginia and has a tentative release date of November 2, 2043.

Barbara Stager of Durham, North Carolina was a churchgoer and apparently devoted wife and mother. On February 1, 1988, she called the police and reported that the gun her husband Russ kept under his pillow when he slept had gone off accidentally and killed him. Subsequent investigation revealed that Stager differed drastically from her public image, given to lying, stealing, excessive spending, and promiscuity. In August 1989, a jury found her guilty of killing Russ and sentenced her to death. After review by a higher court, the death sentence was changed to life imprisonment. Interestingly, her first husband had also died from a gunshot wound in bed, although that death had been classified as accidental.

Mary Flora Bell was born on May 26, 1957 in England. She was unwanted by her mother. First her mother tried to give her away—unsuccessfully—and then to poison her—again unsuccessfully. Meanwhile, her mother exploited her for income by making her perform oral sex on various men. In 1968, at the age of 11, Mary Bell strangled two toddlers to death, perhaps in retribution for the horrors that her mother had visited on her. She was convicted of manslaughter and imprisoned until 1980, when she was 23 years old.

But perhaps *la crème de la crème* of female evildoers was a Hungarian countess who lived during the 16th Century. She had some 600 virgins killed, then bathed in their blood to recapture her youth. "As a cosmetic compound it apparently did not work," Michael Stone, MD, tartly observed.

EVILDOERS AT THE TOP OF THEIR GAME

Just as gender plays a pivotal role in evildoing, the same is the case for age. Most evildoers are young adults. For instance, antisocial personality disorder is most commonly diagnosed in 26-40 year olds. Arsonists tend to be between 18 and 35 years. Most hate crimes are committed by young males.

One reason why may be because people tend to peak intellectually and physically in their young-adult years. Another explanation, Joel Paris, MD, proposes, has to do with impulsivity. In addition to being chair of psychiatry at McGill University in Montreal, Canada, Paris is an expert on personality disorders. People tend to be more impulsive at age 20 than they are at age 40, and people with antisocial personality disorder, which has an impulsivity component, tend to perform fewer antisocial acts as they age, he told me.

Nonetheless, some middle-aged adults have been known to engage in appalling deeds. Take the case of a French carpenter named Michel Fourniret and his wife Monique Olivier. He raped or attempted to rape, then killed seven girls or women when he was 45 to 59 years of age. She helped him do it when she was 38 to 52 years old. They went on trial for these acts in March 2008. In May 2008,

he was convicted of rape and murder in all seven cases and sentenced to life in prison. She was convicted of complicity in four of the murders and also sentenced to life in prison.

Some seniors have been known to do vile things as well. On June 10, 2009, an 88-year-old named James W. von Brunn walked into the US Holocaust Memorial Museum in Washington, DC and killed a security guard with a rifle. His motive? Apparently racial hate. He had been a prolific writer of white supremacist literature. He had also lived briefly in Hayden, Idaho, which for years was home to the Aryan Nations, a racist group run by a neo-Nazi. On January 6, 2010, von Brunn died in prison while awaiting jail.

Juniors, too, have committed malicious acts. On September 19, 2010, an 18-year-old Rutgers University student named Dharun Ravi secretly filmed his male roommate while having sex with another male student and streamed the film on the Internet. He also used social media to invite people to watch the film. In a Twitter message, Ravi wrote: "Roommate asked for the room until midnight. I...turned on my Webcam. I saw him making out with a dude. Yay."

The episode quickly became the subject of gossip in Ravi's dormitory. Three days later, the student who had been surreptitiously filmed—Tyler Clementi—jumped from the George Washington Bridge into the Hudson River in an apparent suicide.

In 2012, Ravi was convicted of bias intimidation and sentenced to 30 days in jail, three years of probation, and 300 hours of community service. He completed all these requirements as of May 30, 2015. As of October 28, 2016, he was working in information technology in New York City and said that he felt relieved that the case was finally behind him.

Nor is grim behavior limited to those age 18 and above. One nationally representative survey identified 284 youth who admitted to fire setting. They were between the ages of 12 and 17 years. Dominique Bourget, MD, an associate professor of psychiatry at the University of Ottawa in Canada, and coworkers examined 64 cases of parricide. Although the perpetrators were, on average, 31 years of age when they killed their fathers, some were as young as 14 when they did so.

In 2013, two Florida girls—one 12 and one 14 were arrested and charged with felony aggravated stalking in connection with the suicide of another 12-year-old, Rebecca Sedgwick. The girls had apparently been sending Sedgwich hateful messages, such as "Drink bleach and die."

Inhumanity can start even younger.

In one case, which took place in Florida, a nine-year-old boy named pushed a toddler into the deep end of a motel swimming pool. As the toddler struggled and sank to the bottom, the boy pulled up a chair to watch. Questioned by the police later, he said that he had simply been curious to see someone drown.

A murderer named Richard Minns had been brought up in a middle-class family in Texas in unremarkable circumstances. Nonetheless, by age eight, he was already sadistic and violent. He made his baby sister swallow a penny. He also placed her near an open window, and when she fell out, he stood by, laughing.

Already by age three, serial sex killer Ted Bundy was starting to act out his murderous fantasies. His aunt, who was then 15 years old, woke up one morning to find Ted lifting the blankets from her bed and sliding a butcher knife in next to her.

If the above reports sound rather improbable, consider this study of 79 preschoolers, with an average age of four years, who had been referred to a behavioral problem clinic for evaluation. Seventy-two percent were found to lose their temper, 58 percent to purposefully annoy others, 41 percent to bully, 32 percent to be vindictive, 28 percent to destroy property, 23 percent to be cruel to others, 20 percent to steal, 20 percent to be cruel to animals, eight percent to set fires, and three percent to engage in forced sexual activity.

Even toddlers may already prep for evildoing, chilling study results reported by University of Colorado researchers in 2013 indicate.

Almost a thousand children between the ages of 14 months and three years of age were evaluated to see how they reacted when their mothers feigned distress. Did they attempt to help or comfort their mothers, or did they ignore, laugh at, or hit their mothers? The children were then scored on symptoms of conduct disorder, such as stealing or torturing animals from ages four to 17. The researchers then looked to see whether there was any connection between how the toddlers had reacted to their mothers' purported distress and whether they had exhibited any signs of conduct disorder in middle childhood or adolescence. The answer was a resounding yes: A lack of empathy predicted later conduct disorder.

Even more striking, these results held even when the gender of the children was taken into the equation. And the same was the case even when the socioeconomic status of the youngsters was considered. Socioeconomic status, like gender and age, can also strongly influence evildoing, as we'll now see.

A NAKED TODDLER IN A BATHTUB

When I was a little girl, my parents and I lived in a lower middle-class neighborhood. Some things happened on our street that trouble me to this day.

A couple living at the end of the street, who despised children, handed out rotten tomatoes on Halloween as treats. I came across two boys pulling legs off a grasshopper one by one. A neighbor heard a toddler living next to her scream unfailingly. She went to the house and knocked. No answer. She tried unlocking the door. No luck. She walked around the house and stopped where the screams seemed to be coming from. It was the bathroom. She went home, brought back a ladder, and managed to climb up and look through the bathroom window. What she saw appalled her. The toddler had been placed nude in a bathtub without water. No one else seemed to be present in the house. She called child protective services, and they came and took the toddler away.

Then when I was 10 years old, we moved into a middle-class neighborhood. Such things didn't seem to happen in our new environment. The worst memory I have from those years is of the dad of a playmate of mine coming to talk with my father because he was having financial problems and his wife was threatening to divorce him for that reason. There were tears in his eyes; I really felt for him.

Scientific evidence seems to confirm my experience: Evildoers often hail from lower socioeconomic strata. For instance, inner-city boys are especially at high risk of becoming adult criminals because of harsh parental discipline, family conflict, neighborhood violence, drugs, and other factors.

Nonetheless, some evildoers do come from more privileged backgrounds.

During the 1960s, Federal Bureau of Investigation (FBI) agents communicated with kidnappers who wanted ransom money. The agents knew that the kidnappers were a man and a woman by their voices. Some smaller details provided even more insights into them. They said that they wanted the ransom money in Eddie Bauer bags; hairs from a Golden Retriever dog were found on one of their letters demanding ransom. The agents concluded that they were a young yuppie couple, no strangers to the good life, including a pedigree dog. And once the agents captured them, their suspects were confirmed.

In 1997, the charred and dismembered torso of a 19-year-old boy were found in a garage in Montgomery County, Maryland, an affluent county bordering Washington, DC. The suspect was a 17-year-old boy named Samuel Sheinbein. His father was a lawyer, and they lived in the neighborhood where the torso was found. Although police quickly got a warrant for Sheinbein's arrest, his father, an Israeli citizen, whisked him off to Israel before he could be arrested. Nonetheless, the Israelis prosecuted him for the crime, found him guilty, and imprisoned him in an Israeli penitentiary. Sixteen years later, when he was 33 years old, he was killed in a shootout in the penitentiary.

In the fall of 2001—as if Americans hadn't already been traumatized enough by the terrorist attacks on September 11—envelopes containing spores from the deadly anthrax bacterium were mailed to some lawmakers on Capitol Hill as well as to some other recipients. The spores killed five people and injured 17 others. Authorities suspected that the perpetrator was a scientist who was trying to develop a vaccine against anthrax infection. However, it took them seven years to amass enough evidence to file charges against him. Just as they were about to do so, however, he died by apparent suicide.

Then in April 2016, *CBS Evening News* reported this bombshell: Dennis Hastert, the longest-serving Republican House speaker in history, confessed to having sexual molested boys he had coached a number of years earlier. Referring to Hastert as a "serial child molester," a federal judge imposed on him a sentence of 15 months in prison, two years of supervised release, and a $250,000 fine. Hastert was imprisoned in 2016 and released 13 months later. He was 75 years old.

There you have it. Privilege, fame, and fortune are no shields against evildoing. But they are no bulwark against being punished for it either.

PARTNERS IN CRIME OR GOING IT ALONE

Our prototypal evildoer is now coming into focus. It's a male, young, from a not very classy background. But how about tying the knot: Does matrimony play any role in the equation?

Our evildoer is more likely to be single than married. For example, serial killers are rarely married, and when they are, usually not very successfully, evildoer expert Michael Stone, MD, found. That doesn't mean, though, that he is devoid of female pleasure or female devotion.

Remember Myra Hindley who lured little children onto the moor in England so that her paramour, serial sexual killer Ian Brady, could have a go at them, then slaughter them?

How about Monique Olivier, mentioned above, who gained the confidence of little girls so that her husband could prey on them?

And how about that infamous outlaw couple, Bonnie and Clyde, who terrorized the heartland of America during the 1930s? Both Bonnie (Elizabeth Park) and Clyde (Clyde Barrow) were young and wild and undoubtedly slept together, even though Bonnie was married to somebody else. During the two years that she acted as his companion, she may or may not have shot anyone, but it's clear that she "stood by her man" as he and his gang went about murdering eight people, kidnapping seven people, robbing six banks, and engaging in scores of armed robberies and auto thefts.

When male evildoers do marry, it can dampen their blood lust, at least if the marriage lasts. But what is more questionable is whether they are likely to reform if they marry a woman who also has a criminal history. A Danish study published in the April 2015 *Journal of Marriage and Family* says No. A Norwegian study published in the May 2014 *British Journal of Criminology* says Yes. The deciding factor may be the woman – whether she has decided, upon committing to marriage, to forego a life of crime for a law-abiding one.

EVILDOING AND EQUAL OPPORTUNITY

Just as evildoers may change their behaviors after marriage, evildoer behaviors in general may change as well, in a sense ebbing and flowing with the times.

Before 1850, serial sex killing was virtually nonexistent in Western society. Toward the end of the 19th Century it became more noticeable with cases like Jack the Ripper in London. And even though it is still a rare phenomenon, it has increased tenfold since the 1960's. The Women's Liberation Movement, which started in the 1960's and which has soared since, might have been one contributory factor, evildoer expert Michael Stone, MD, suspects.

Serial sex killers, he points out, come mostly from the lower to middle class. Men who emotionally, physically, and/or sexually abuse their wives and partners do too. As women from this class have increasingly been able to find suitable employment, they have been able to leave abusive husbands and partners. As a result, some abusive partners or husbands may have switched to targeting women they don't know to vent their hatred of women and their desire to dominate them.

Women's liberation may also be contributing to debauchery among the "fair sex." For some decades now, such behaviors have increased among women. Females are doing many of the same vile things these days that males are doing, such as joining gangs or serving as suicide bombers. A few have even become serial killers. During the 1990's, Aileen Carol Wuornos was a 34-year-old hitchhiking prostitute. She became known as the "Damsel of Death" because she robbed and murdered men who gave her a lift. She was ultimately caught and put on trial. She pleaded guilty to seven murders and was sentenced to death. In 2002, she was executed by lethal injection

School shootings in the United States are other phenomena that were largely nonexistent before the 1990's. Since then, they have increased to a disturbing degree. One probable explanation for this upswing is a contagion or copycat effect, some researchers propose, because suicides often increase after publicized suicide events. Another is easy access to guns: School shooters have often been later found to own a lot of weapons. A third is violent video or computer games: School shooters have often been later found to have large collections of them.

But it's not just contagion, guns, or violent games that seem to be stoking the recent flood in school shootings in the United States. Rage seems to be doing so as well. As one school shooter later explained: "I am not insane, I am angry. The world has shit on me for the final time. I am not spoiled or lazy, for murder is not weak and slow, it is gutsy and daring."

NINE
CAN YOU TELL AN EVILDOER BY HIS LOOKS?

Across San Francisco Bay, on a promontory in San Marin County, you can see an ochre-colored stone fortress glimmering in the California sun. It is San Quentin State Prison, where some of America's most wicked are housed.

One day a few years ago, through my work with *Psychiatric News*, I managed to join a small private tour of the prison. We passed through all sorts of security gates—truly, it seemed like a medieval fortress!—and found ourselves in what appeared to be an inner court-yard. Lots of male prisoners were milling about. Most were young. Many looked lean and mean. But some were good-looking hunks, or what some women call "hot."

We were then led deeper into the bowels of the prison, and at one point, a handcuffed death-row prisoner was escorted past us by two guards. He was short, stocky, looked to be maybe 60 years old, and was not somebody I'd want to meet in a dark alley, but no mon-ster in appearance either. For a second—a split second—our gazes crossed. *What are you thinking?* I wondered. *What ghastly deeds have earned you a private cell on death row?*

Can you tell an evildoer by his looks?

Psychology research findings can help us interpret facial expressions and body language. For example, both a real and a fake smile pull up the corners of the mouth, but a real smile also includes a wrinkling of the crows' feet at the corners of the eyes. A dynamic change in a person's mouth expression can distract you from noticing a change in their eye expression. Subtle changes in facial expression often reflect deceit, but they occur so fast that most of us fail to notice them. Certain gestures may indicate that a person is lying (See Chapter 11).

Such insights in turn can help us spot evildoers. But beyond that, forensic experts and forensic science offer us devilishly little guidance in how to identify them by their looks.

My own take, based on what I saw in San Quentin Prison, is that sometimes, depraved individuals look the way you'd expect them to look; other times they may possibly look the part, and yet in still other instances, they don't look that way at all. This is also my impression after studying the photos of some infamous evildoers. Here are some details from my informal photo survey.

THREE WITCHES FROM *MACBETH*

One wanton individual who definitely looked the part was Joseph Vacher, the 19th Century French shepherd boy killer introduced in Chapter 6. Vacher had a red eye and a partially deformed face.

On August 9, 1969, a housekeeper reported for work at film director Roman Polanski's home in Hollywood, California and found five bodies slashed and bloodied. The victims had been beaten and stabbed a number of times. The word "PIG" had been scrawled in blood on the front door. Eventually the leader of the massacre, Charles Manson, and three of his acolytes who assisted him— Susan Atkins, Patricia Krenwinkel, and Leslie Van Houten—were apprehended, found guilty, and sentenced to death. But their sentences were commuted to life in prison after the California Supreme Court abolished capital punishment in 1972.

A photo taken of these three young women on their way to the courtroom before sentencing is chilling. One is strutting with her head held high, a smile of satisfaction lighting her face. A second is cackling. A third has placed her hands over her breast in mock remorse and meanwhile is convulsed with laughter. They look like three witches from *Macbeth*—which, in a sense, they were.

An evildoer who fit the script during the 1980s was Richard Ramenez. He beat, mutilated, and murdered 13 people in Southern California before he was apprehended. At first glance, the "Night Stalker," as he was known, was dashingly handsome with jet-black hair, onyx eyes, high cheekbones, and wide, sensuous lips. But at second glance, you could see that his eyes spewed venom, and that his lips curled down in contempt

The 1990's "rogues' gallery" featured a mathematician named Ted Kaczynski (introduced in Chapter 4). He had fabricated and exploded 16 bombs, killing three people and wounding 23 others before he was caught in the mid-1990s. Despite his intelligence, the so-called Unibomber was a hairy, hermit living in a rustic shed in rural Montana. Furthermore, his eyes were spooky. He didn't look at you, but through you, at what appeared to be a dark and desolate world. He looked like what he was—a loathsome individual.

The year 2012 saw two mass shootings in the United States. Both were carried out by young men whose faces, as well as behaviors, probably should have tipped people off that they represented danger.

One was Adam Lanza of Newtown, Connecticut. Although Lanza was an honors student in high school, both teachers and students noticed that he was fidgety, socially withdrawn, and without friends. Moreover, his face indicated that something was terribly amiss with him. He wore a page-boy haircut with bangs falling over his forehead. His large brown eyes stared straight ahead as if he had been startled or spaced out, and his mouth hung agape. On December 14, 2012, he killed his mother in their Newtown home, then drove to the Sandy Hook Elementary School in Newton, where he fatally shot 20 children and six adult staff members before taking his own life. The reasons for Lanza's actions remain unclear.

The other was James Holmes, who killed 12 people and injured 70 others in an Aurora, Colorado movie theatre on July 20, 2012. A photo taken of Holmes in 2013, after he had been apprehended, shows a young man with bushy brown hair, a bushy brown beard, and large brown eyes that stare into space, sort of spaced out, just as Adam Lanza's had. It's pretty clear that something is seriously wrong with him. When Holmes went on trial in 2015, one court-appointed psychiatrist diagnosed him with schizoaffective disorder, another with schizotypal personality disorder. Both, however, concurred that he had been sane when he plotted and carried out his shootings and thus should be held accountable for them. Their testimony helped sway the jury to convict him of first-degree murder. He was sentenced to life imprisonment without the possibility of parole.

MANY FACES AREN'T SO TRANSPARENT

Yet many evildoer countenances—perhaps the majority—don't reflect the character and intentions of their owners as clearly as those described above.

During the 1960s, in northwestern England, a young store clerk named Ian Brady, briefly introduced in Chapter 3, undertook some diabolical acts with the help of his girlfriend Myra Hindley. They abducted four children. Brady then tortured them, sexually molested them, slit their throats, and finally buried them in a moor near Manchester. On October 6, 1965, however, someone came across Brady while he was killing a fifth child. The witness raced to the police and reported that Brady had "hit the lad on the left side of his head with a hatchet," that "it was a terribly hard blow," and that "it sounded horrible." The police arrested Brady hours later. A trial judge later declared that Brady "was wicked beyond redemption." Indeed, Brady showed no remorse for his truculent acts until he died, at the age of 79, in a high-security psychiatric hospital in Liverpool, England. Could Brady's appearance in the months before his malfeasance have given any indication of what he was about? Not necessarily. He seemed to take pride in his appearance; he wore a hairpiece and a snappy sports jacket on the day the police drove him to court. On the other hand, his bearing was haughty, his eyes cold and distant, and his thin, wide lips curved down in contempt, suggesting that he was a nefarious character, someone not to be trifled with.

Then during 1976-1977 in New York City, normally jaded New Yorkers found themselves being terrorized by a serial killer who called himself the "Son of Sam." During the night or predawn hours, he would shoot women or couples in their cars. The Son of Sam was eventually apprehended and turned out to be a young postal clerk from Yonkers, New York named David Berkowitz. Could Berkowitz's appearance have tipped people off that he was a danger? Probably not at first glance: He had a chubby cherubic face. But perhaps at second glance: His narrow-set dark eyes could assume a stealthy look, and his rosebud lips could tilt up in a smug smile.

Now we move on to the American Midwest to Wichita, Kansas where a serial killer left his mark from 1974 on up to 1991.

His name was Dennis Rader, and from many accounts, he seemed to be a regular guy growing up in a normal family, eventually obtaining a bachelor's degree from Kansas State University, marrying, having two daughters, serving as president of his church council and as a Cub Scout leader.

Rader, however, also pursued a secret life. As a child, he tortured and killed animals and fantasized about capturing and torturing women. Eventually he turned his fantasizes into reality and, between 1974 and 1991, tortured and killed 10 people, mostly women, earning the moniker "the Bind, Torture, and Kill" (BTK) murderer. As part of his work for ADT Security Services in Wichita, he installed security alarms in homes, and it was often at the behest of homeowners afraid of the BTK murderer, that is, himself! He bragged about his exploits in letters that he mailed to the police and local newspapers. This braggadocio eventually led to his arrest on February 25, 2005. He was tried, convicted, and on August 18, 2005, sentenced to 10 consecutive life sentences. Today he is serving those sentences in solitary confinement in the El Dorado Correctional Facility in Kansas.

Apparently, everyone who knew Rader was shocked to learn that he was the BTK serial killer. But could his appearance have given people some indication of his lethal potential? Not necessarily, but possibly, I believe. A snapshot taken of him as a young man suggests that he was quite handsome with symmetrically placed, well-proportioned features. His eyebrows are nicely arched; his nose straight, with a slight upward tilt at the end; his lips wide and sensitive, and his chin firm. But oh, those eyes! They bore right into you, conveying abrasiveness and cruelty. And a photo taken of him as an older man, right after his arrest, is even more of a giveaway to his true character. His eyes still reflect hostility and viciousness, but, in addition, his previously appealing wide, sensitive lips are now turned down in a scowl.

Back in 1991, as the BTK serial killer was winding down his atrocities, an 11-year-old girl in Placerville, California was snatched from a bus stop. Her name was Jaycee Lee Dugard. The disappearance of the wholesome looking, pretty little blond was a nightmare for not just her mother, but her stepfather. Moreover, since he had been the last person to see her before her abduction, the police suspected that he was the perpetrator. The suspicions swirling around him destroyed his marriage.

The case was never solved—that is, until something dramatic happened 18 years later. On August 26, 2009, someone reported to a San Francisco Bay area police station that he had seen a convicted sex offender named Phillip Garrido with two children in the University of California, Berkeley area. The police interviewed Garrido and eventually got him to admit that he had kidnapped Dugard 18 years earlier, and that he had fathered the two children with her. Furthermore, it turned out that Garrido, with the help of his wife Nancy, had held Dugard as a slave in their backyard many years, and that the two children Garrido fathered with her had never been to school or seen a doctor.

Both Garridos were arrested, and the next day, Dugard was reunited with her mother, who was overjoyed that she was still alive. Her stepfather was also thrilled when he got the news and also relieved that he had finally been cleared of suspicions regarding her disappearance.

I'm looking at two mug shots taken of the Garridos at the time of their arrest—when he was 58 years old and she 54. He looks a bit rough, but not obviously decadent. Actually he appears rather intelligent, and his light blue eyes reflect a certain pathos, a haunted look, and his thin lips suggest sensitivity. She, in contrast, appears a deadbeat, not very intelligent, with a drooping left eyelid and a resigned, firm mouth. If I had to place a bet based on looks which of the two was the more malevolent, I would place it on her, even though he was probably the brains behind the operation.

On May 29, 2014, a family photo of a 17-year-old named Lauren A. Bush appeared in *The Washington Post.* The photo shows a teen without very appealing facial features and long, rather unkempt dishwasher blond hair. But she's bosomy, and her hand placed on her hip indicates that she thinks she is pretty hot stuff. She confessed to having repeatedly assaulted a 16-year-old autistic boy. She and another girl also filmed him while encouraging him to have sex with his family's dog. The judge hearing her case called it "chilling." Could Bush's appearance have alerted people to her despicable character? Maybe. Or maybe not.

And then 2018 brought a case to public attention that dwarfed those described above in cruelty, and once again, the perpetrators' appearance may or may not have mirrored their depravity potential.

David Allen Turpin was an engineer working for Northrop Grumman and making good money. He, his wife Louisa, and their 13 children lived in a quiet neighborhood in Riverside County, California, about 70 miles east of Los Angeles. Shortly before sunrise on January 14, 2018, one of their children, a 17-year-old, climbed out a window of the house, raced off, and dialed 911. Deputies from the Riverside County Sheriff's Department met with her. She told them that she and her siblings were being held in the house against their will. The deputies visited the house and found 12 young people, from ages two to 29, living under horrific conditions. They were malnourished. Some were shackled in the dark to their beds with chains and padlocks. All were rescued and brought to a hospital for care.

On January 19, 2018, David and Louise Turpin appeared in court and entered "not guilty" pleas to more than three dozen charges regarding torture, abuse, false imprisonment, and incest of their children. A photo taken of him at this time shows a 57-year-old man with a mane of thick silver hair falling to his shoulders. His face is elongated, his features well proportioned. A grey beard is starting to sprout above his small, heart-shaped lips and on his firm chin and rather full cheeks. At first glance, you might think that he is a musician or artist. But at second glance, you would probably have a much more disturbing impression because his rather narrow-set brown eyes are crafty, surly, spewing hate. A photo taken of his wife at this time shows a 49-year-old woman with long brown hair, greying a bit at the hairline. She has large brown eyes; a pert, slightly turned-up nose; and high cheekbones—the makings of an attractive face. Yet the look in her eyes is hard and hostile, and her mouth curls down in a combative manner. She doesn't look as reprehensible as her husband, but not appealing either.

YOU'D PROBABLY NEVER GUESS

Finally, let's take a look at a face that I would never have connected with evildoing, but then, if you're particularly observant, perhaps you would have.

The face belongs to a Houston, Texas woman named Susan Wright. A photo taken of her in March 2004 shows a pretty young blond with friendly blue eyes, a friendly smile, and yes, some creases at the outer edge of her eyes, suggesting that the smile was genuine. Yet she had done something incredibly vile on January 13, 2003.

That evening, while her husband was enjoying a cocaine high, she lured him into their bedroom and, while pretending to make love to him on the bed, tied his limbs to the bed's headboard and foot board. She then raised a knife, took a swipe at his penis, and stabbed him in the chest 193 times. She buried his body in the backyard in hopes of camouflaging her crime. It didn't work. She was convicted of first-degree murder in 2004 and is currently serving a 20-year sentence. She was denied parole in 2014 and 2017.

Wright claimed that she killed her husband because she was

tired of his cocaine-fueled rages, where he kicked, pounded, and slapped her.

So, all things considered, there is no easy way to identify evil-doers by their looks. "Depraved individuals look pretty much like you and me," a forensic psychiatrist told me. He should know if anybody does: In addition to visiting death row prisoners, his father was murdered when he was a boy.

And if depraved individuals look pretty much like you and me, does that mean that they could be your coworkers, your neighbors, your relatives or friends?

TEN
STRANGERS OR PEOPLE YOU KNOW?

Even with all the mass shootings sweeping across America, it never dawned on me that a shooter would set his sights on my hometown.

But on June 28, 2018, that's what happened. Annapolis, Maryland is a charming historic town perched at the intersection of the Severn River and the Chesapeake Bay and home to the United States Naval Academy. And it was the scene of a mass shooting that made international headlines.

When I first heard about the tragedy from a neighbor that hot sunny day, my first reaction was shock. My second thought was: *Gosh, it happened only several miles from where I live.* And then: *Was anybody I know involved?* As things played out, it turned out that I did.

The Annapolis shooting also set the stage for a larger question: How many evildoers are strangers, and how many do you know?

The answer, in part, depends on the type of deed carried out, forensic scientists tell us.

For instance, many child molesters know their victims. Yet those who abduct their victims usually do not. They are almost all men. They tend to be unmarried, to have few friends, to be seedy, unattractive, social outcasts. Since they lack the interpersonal skills to attract, befriend, and seduce their victims, they resort to abduction.

Although girls are generally raised to be wary of strange men, they are usually not taught to be vigilant regarding those men they know. Yet more than half of the men who rape women are known to them, one national women's study showed: Twenty percent are friends, 16 percent husbands, 14 percent boyfriends, and 9 percent neighbors, coworkers, handymen, or other acquaintances.

Ninety percent of the individuals who exploit the elderly financially are family members or other people the victims know well, such as caretakers, neighbors, or friends, the National Center on Elder Abuse estimates. One unscrupulous lawyer even raided the finances of an older client until he was caught.

Most male serial killers target strangers. However, the situation is more complex as far as female serial killers are concerned. Elizabeth Gurian of the Institute of Criminology at the University of Cambridge in England studied 65 cases of female serial killers from countries as diverse as Australia, France, India, Mexico, Russia, and the United States. Thirty-five had acted alone; the remaining 30 had acted with one or more male partners. The sole female serial killers, Gurian found, had mostly murdered family members of either gender and had dispatched them with poisons or medications. The partnered female serial killers, in contrast, had mostly killed female strangers and done so with blunt force, guns, or strangulation.

Male and female stalkers also tend to target different types of victims, Australian forensic researchers have found. Female stalkers usually focus on those with whom they have had professional contact, especially psychiatrists, psychologists, and family physicians, although teachers and legal professionals are occasional targets. Male stalkers, in contrast, pursue a much wider range of victims—not just professionals, but prior intimate partners, acquaintances, and even strangers.

And when it comes to the seriously mentally ill who murder, there, too, you may possibly find gender differences. California researchers compared the records of 47 women who had murdered or had attempted to murder yet had been found not guilty by reason of insanity, to the records of 47 men with the same profile. Most of the women's victims had been family members—often children—whereas most of the men's victims had been friends, acquaintances, or strangers. However, a study conducted by Pennsylvania researchers of 95 male murderers with severe mental illness produced different findings: Most had killed family members, partners, or lovers.

MOTIVE CAN ALSO INFLUENCE VICTIM CHOICE

Motive can also influence whether evildoers target strangers or people they know.

Two-thirds of child abductions are carried out for sexual pleasure. The others are conducted for other reasons – say, ransom, or because a carjacker inadvertently drives off with a child in the back seat.

About 20 percent of mass murders are carried out by disgruntled workers, another 11 percent are spurred by hate.

Female serial killers who go solo are more likely to kill for a purpose, for example, profit, religion, or because they are a member of a cult, than out of a lust for power or sexual pleasure. A good example is serial killer Aileen Wuornos. She would hitch rides with truck drivers, then rob and kill them.

In contrast, a lust for power and/or sex often propels male serial killers and, consequently, shapes their victim choice. A prime example is serial killer Dennis Rader of Wichita, Kansas, introduced in the previous chapter.

From 1974 to 1991, he selected, mostly randomly, victims whom he thought would fulfill his needs. Most of the victims were women, but not all. Chance also played a role. In one case, he had targeted his victims, a family, and had even cut their phone lines. However, he hadn't figured out how to get into the house and was thinking of changing his plans, when a child in the family opened the front door to let the family dog in. The front door was his entry, he decided.

Throughout his serial-killing career, Rader not only stalked, but bound and tortured his victims, then shot, stabbed, strangled, or choked them to death. After he was apprehended and admitted to his grisly acts, he claimed that sexual fantasy had driven him to do what he had done—that he had masturbated after strangling at least one victim with her pantyhose. However, a hunger for power also seems to have played a role, because throughout his serial-killing years, he had sent taunting letters to the police and press, referring to himself as the notorious B.T.K. Killer (the "B.T.K." standing for "bind, torture, and kill"). And in one of his letters, he demanded, "How many do I have to kill before I get my name in the paper or [receive] some national attention?"

BY THEIR ACTS YOU MAY NOT KNOW THEM

Even though Rader's serial slaughters spanned the 1970s to the 1990s, it wasn't until 2005 that he was finally identified and apprehended. Why did it take people in Wichita so long to realize that he was the infamous B.T.K. Killer? Undoubtedly because there were many reasons to believe that he was just the guy next door and a pretty good Joe at that. He was married, the father of two, a former Boy Scout leader and a regular churchgoer.

Actually, more evildoers than you would think are leading what appear to be exemplary lives.

Rapists are often articulate, highly intelligent men who have good jobs, wives or girlfriends, and get along well with others, Robert Simon, MD, a forensic psychiatrist affiliated with Georgetown University, reports. "Thus, rapists do not appear to be very different from the rest of us," he observes.

When forensic psychiatrists are scheduled to interview a murderer for the first time, they often expect to encounter a "blood-dripping monster," Simon points out. But instead, what they usually find "is a quiet, reasonably cooperative guy-next-door type of individual," uncomfortably like themselves.

Serial killer John Wayne Gacy raped, sodomized, tortured, and strangled to death 33 men. He managed to do so while running a prosperous construction business, marrying twice, and becoming a public benefactor. As a member of the Jolly Jokers Club, he created the character of Pogo the Clown, and as Pogo, he traveled to hospitals to cheer sick children. He was even voted by his local Jaycees club its outstanding member for 1967.

Serial killer Ted Bundy, who killed at least 35 women, was a lawyer. His friends saw him on the fast track to high political office, such as senator or governor. His girlfriends were smitten by his attentiveness. He would send them flowers and write them love poems.

Spouses can also be deceived. Federal Bureau of Investigation spy Robert Hanssen was a devoted husband and father and from all outward appearances a devout Catholic. Yet he betrayed his country by selling valuable information to the Russians. He also betrayed his wife by associating with hookers and by inviting a friend to secretly watch while he had sex with her.

Even the experts can be fooled. Henry Hubbard of Seattle, Washington appeared to be a model police officer. His fellow police officers noticed that he acted kind and caring toward the women with whom he had contact. Yet Hubbard was also a vicious rapist. When his colleagues learned that, they were shocked.

DETOURS IN VICTIM CHOICE CAN DIFFUSE SUSPICION

Discerning the evildoers among us can be even tougher if they not only do not fit our preconceived notions but target more than one type of victim. A prime example is the 2018 Annapolis, Maryland mass shooter, a young man named Jarrod Ramos.

Jarrod Ramos had long, black hair; an elongated face with finely chiseled, one might say aristocratic features—heavy black eyebrows, deep-set black eyes, a long, thin nose and a sensitive mouth—and with just a trace of whiskers above his lips and on his chin. He was also well-educated with a degree in computer engineering, and he held down a good job; he worked for the federal Bureau of Labor Statistics. Yet something was amiss with his psyche.

In 2009, he reconnected with a former high-school classmate on Facebook, yet in 2010, when she tried to break away from him, he got angry and vulgar and even started stalking her. In 2011, she sought the assistance of an Annapolis lawyer named Brennan McCarthy (whom I happened to know). With McCarthy's help, she brought a harassment case against Ramos. Ramos now turned his anger toward McCarthy. One evening, McCarthy's wife spied Ramos hiding in the bushes outside their house. She was terrified.

Just days after Ramos pleaded guilty to the charge, the Annapolis newspaper, *The Capital Gazette,* published an article about the harassment case. Ramos now directed his rage toward the newspaper. In 2012, he filed a lawsuit against the owners of the newspaper, claiming that it had defamed him, even though he had pleaded guilty to the harassment charge. A judge dismissed the case. But Ramos continued to seethe with fury, posting threats against *The Capital* on social media.

At some point during 2017, he legally purchased a shotgun. Neither his harassment conviction nor his threats were a barrier to buying a weapon.

On June 28, Ramos stormed his way into the editorial offices of *The Capital,* brandishing the shotgun. He shot five people dead and injured several others. When McCarthy learned of the slaughter, he exclaimed, "I bet the killer was Ramos!" McCarthy had guessed right.

We can also be caught off guard if evildoers are people in positions of authority.

Back during the 1990's, Harold Shipman, MD, practiced family medicine in Hyde, a city in northern England. He appeared to be the ideal family doctor. He had twinkly eyes; wore glasses; sported a beard, and was soft-spoken, calm, quiet, and friendly. He even made home visits.

What neither his wife and children nor the community suspected was that the home visits gave him the perfect opportunity to snuff out the lives of his elderly patients. He would smile and chat with them while asking them to roll up a sleeve so that he could give them something for pain. He ended their lives with massive, fatal injections.

In 1998, the authorities became suspicious of Shipman because so many of his elderly patients had died. In 2000, he was convicted of murdering 15 of them. There was reason to suspect that he had killed up to 215 of them.

His motive or motives will never be known since he hung himself in prison in 2004. It may have been that he wanted to exert a God-like power over life and death, or that he wanted to relieve his elderly patients' suffering. But one thing's for sure: He betrayed his patients because none of them had asked him to end their lives.

And would you ever suspect any of the parents you know to be capable of killing their own children? Yet it happens.

I'll never forget the time my husband and I were invited into the home of a business acquaintance of his, and a photo of a lovely young woman and two children was prominently displayed in the living room. I assumed the photo was a picture of his wife and children, yet he made no mention of them. Only later did I learn that his wife had killed both of the children before taking her own life.

Pretty shocking stuff. Yet research has shown that people are more likely to be murdered before age five than at any other time in their lives, and usually by a parent. Studies have also divulged that while mothers and fathers are equally likely to kill their own off-spring, their motives often differ.

Women who kill their children during the first 24 hours of life almost always do so because they don't want the baby. Women who kill their children when the children are older may do so because they suffer from a severe mental illness such as schizophrenia, schizoaffective illness, major depression, or bipolar disorder. Some men who kill their children also do so because of serious mental illness. Others, however, do so as part of child abuse, or because they want to take revenge against the child's mother.

And yet: Even though the evildoers among us may not look or act the part, and even if they are diabolically clever at covering their tracks, surely there must be some ways we can identify them? Yes, there are.

ELEVEN
SOME RED FLAGS
REGARDING EVILDOERS

August 17, 1998 was a pivotal day for President Bill Clinton. He testified before a federal grand jury that he "did not have sexual relations with that woman, that is, White House intern Monica Lewinsky.

His disavowal was later found to be false and to lead to his impeachment as president. It also led to something that he probably never imagined: a study concerning the body language of liars.

Now granted, the study was only a case study. Nonetheless, it was fascinating and potentially of practical value. Lying is a warning sign that someone is capable of harming you. Indeed, it is one of the hallmarks of antisocial individuals, including those especially virulent antisocial individuals known as psychopaths.

Here is how the study came about.

Clinton's grand jury testimony was televised on that fateful day of August 17, 1998. One of the Americans who happened to see it was a colorful and somewhat controversial psychiatrist-neurologist named Alan Hirsch, MD. Hirsch operated the Smell and Taste Research and Treatment Foundation in Chicago. Hirsch noticed that

Clinton frequently touched his nose during his testimony. Hirsch likewise knew that nose touching was suspected of being a physical sign of lying. Hirsch then came up with the novel idea of using Clinton's grand jury testimony to explore the body language of liars.

Hirsch's partner in this undertaking was Charles J. Wolf, MD. He too was affiliated with the Smell and Taste Research and Treatment Foundation. First, they identified, from the psychiatric and law-enforcement literature, 23 behaviors indicating that somebody might be lying. Sixteen were nonverbal and seven verbal. After that, they determined the number of times these behaviors appeared in a segment of Clinton's grand jury testimony that was later found to be false. They also determined the number of times these behaviors appeared under two control conditions. One was a segment of his grand jury testimony where he answered routine factual questions and where a lie would have been easily detected. The other was one of his fundraising speeches where he was probably telling the truth. Finally, the researchers compared the former findings to the latter ones.

The result: Nineteen out of 23 of the behaviors were present significantly more often in the mendacious segment than in the truthful segment of the grand jury testimony. Twenty out of 23 were present significantly more often in the mendacious segment of the grand jury testimony than in the fundraising speech.

Some of the behaviors found to increase during Clinton's lying were averting one's gaze after making eye contact; throat clearing; speech errors; drinking and swallowing; leaning forward or engaging in postural shifts; crossing arms; handling objects; denying lying or emphasizing the truthfulness of one's answers by prefacing them with words or phrases such as "honestly," "as far as I know," or "believe me"; and, yes, touching one's nose.

They published their results in the October-December 2001

Journal of the American Academy of Psychiatry and the Law. Obviously the findings need to be replicated in studies with more subjects before the behaviors linked with lying in the Clinton tape can also be considered lying indicators in the general population. But if the behaviors that signaled lying by Clinton could be confirmed in other subjects, they might prove to be valuable tools not just for mental health professionals and police officers, but for all of us in spotting mendacity.

LYING: MORE THAN SKIN DEEP

Yet lying entails more than just body language. Insights regarding some other aspects of lying can also help us spot liars, figure out why they aren't telling the truth, and decide how we should deal with them.

For example, why do people lie?

Lying is "conscious and deliberate," Howard Owens, MD, a forensic psychiatrist affiliated with Bellevue Hospital in New York City, reported at a 2010 meeting of the American Psychoanalytical Association. "But there are many other ways of clouding the truth that are not conscious and deliberate."

Defendants and witnesses sometimes don't tell the truth because they are mistaken about what actually happened, other times because they have different perceptions of viewed events, and still others to save face or avoid punishment, Owens noted. Also, defendants and witnesses may do what many people outside the forensic arena do: tell lies to make others feel good or to spare them pain.

Some people lie to feel better about themselves, Cornell University psychiatrist Richard Friedman, MD, points out. Exaggerating their accomplishments is one way to bolster their fragile self- esteem. Remember the film *Catch Me If You Can* with actors Leonardo Dicaprio and Tom Hanks? A young man successfully passes himself off as a pilot, a lawyer, and a doctor, following in the footsteps of his father, who was also a fraud. He presumably engages in such activities to boost both his father's and his own ego. The tale is based on a true story.

Still other people engage in what the experts call pathological lying. They tell the same lies over a number of years until they start to believe the fabrications themselves. The motives underlying pathological lying are obscure. Self-aggrandizement doesn't seem to play a role. Moreover, pathological lying is distinct from two other conditions known as malingering and confabulation, Charles Dike, MD, a Yale University forensic psychiatrist, reports. Malingering is an intentional attempt to create physical or psychological symptoms; confabulation is an attempt used by some individuals with amnesia to fill memory gaps with made-up material.

Information obtained from brain-imaging studies may likewise give us some assist in spotting liars and in dealing with them.

Daniel Langleben, MD, of the University of Pennsylvania and his team used functional MRI imaging to track the brain activity of volunteers while they were either lying or telling the truth about a certain playing card. The same two areas in their brains moved into gear whether they were lying or not, but these brain areas revved up even more while they were lying. Functional MRI research has shown that telling a lie takes about three times more brain effort than telling the truth does, Robert Granacher, Jr., MD, a University of Kentucky forensic psychiatrist, told me. As a result, it may eventually be possible to use fMRI imaging to determine whether people on trial or testifying at trial are telling the truth, he noted.

Moreover, a small but intriguing study conducted by Texas researchers suggests that the gut might mirror whether people are lying or not. The researchers used an electrogastrogram (EGG) machine to record gastrointestinal wave activity in 16 healthy volunteers during three periods: a resting baseline activity, a truth-telling period, and a lying period, then compared the results for each subject. The subjects experienced a marked increase in abnormal gastric wave activity while lying, but not during the other two test periods.

Now, we obviously can't peer into people's brains, or guts, to see whether they are fabricating stories. But perhaps certain body movements—for example, clearing the throat, taking a sip of water, shifting posture, or diddling with a pen—might indicate that their brains, or guts, are working overtime to deceive. After all, those are some of the body postures Clinton engaged in while lying.

In any event, perhaps because reading body language to determine lying is far from a science, most of us aren't all that good at using it for this purpose. Even the experts come up short: Psychiatrists, for instance, have been found only 57 percent accurate at recognizing deception, which is only a tad better than chance.

But it isn't just a difficulty in reading body language that makes it so tough for most of us to detect mendacity. Another reason, it appears, is our mindset.

Take the case of scams, unproven medical treatments, or empty political promises. Why do many people fall for such deceptions? Anton Kris, MD, a professor of psychiatry at Harvard Medical School, gave some thought to this question. He decided that four different conditions have to be present for it to happen: an idealization of authority, a yearning for certainty, a strong desire to obtain something, and excessive trust.

And yet another reason why so many of us are vulnerable to lying is that con artists, predators, and other evildoers can be incredibly skilled at hoodwinking. Glen Gabbard, MD, a Baylor College of Medicine professor of psychiatry, experienced this firsthand while working in the prison system. If you think you are too smart to be fooled by such people, think again, he warns us. "Nobody is such a good clinician that he or she can never get conned. You can have all the training in the world and still get taken."

CHARM: ANOTHER RED FLAG

Lying is not the only behavior that people use to deceive. There is also charm—one of the diagnostic criteria for both antisocial personality disorder and psychopathy. If you doubt the potential toxicity of charm, take a look at the following true stories.

During and after World War I, in the town of Gambais, France, a man named Landru courted one woman after another. Each fell for him because of his allure and good manners. And each—altogether 10 in number—disappeared after succumbing to his charms.

Eventually the good people of Gambais began to make a connection between Landru and the vanishing ladies. Particularly unsettling was a putrid smell emanating from his chimney from time to time. Could he be murdering, then burning the women? Finally, the police came knocking at his door, searched his house, and excavated his yard, looking for any evidence that might link him to the murders. They found human bones buried in his yard. Although the bones were not identified specifically as those of the missing women, they were enough evidence for the police to arrest him, charge him with murder, and put him on trial. A jury found him guilty, and he was executed in 1922.

During the 1970s, there was a suave and handsome one-time law student named Ted Bundy (introduced in previous chapters). He crisscrossed the United States enticing, then murdering between 36 and 100 women, including several in a Chi Omega sorority in Florida.

On April 20, 1999, the teens Eric Harris and Dylan Klebold (also mentioned earlier) stormed into Columbine High School in Columbine, Colorado, then killed 12 students, a teacher, and finally themselves. The slaughter shocked not only the public, but people who knew Harris and Klebold. Why hadn't they seen this coming?

One reason why may have been because Harris had been smooth and well-mannered. "That boy was very skilled at deception," the mother of one of the Columbine students recalled. Even when Harris engaged in some troubling antisocial acts such as cracking the windshield of a neighbor and then urinating on his bushes, Harris managed to convince his father that these were trivial misdemeanors. "Eric fooled them all. He fooled everyone," the neighbor said.

Even younger children can bewitch and deceive. A disturbing tale about one such child was reported in *The New York Times* on May 11, 2012.

A boy named Michael started doing some deeply troubling things at age three, shortly after his younger brother was born. He would shriek and scream for hours on end. All sorts of things seemed to set him off. By age five, he was still engaging in rages, but had developed another unnerving facility as well. He could switch from fury to pure rationality or to what appeared to be calculated charm. By the time Michael reached age nine, his parents had taken him to numerous mental health professionals, and each had given him a different diagnosis. Finally, the last professional suggested that Michael might be a fledgling psychopath.

Now, the notion that a young child can already display psychopathic tendencies such as charm and deception is certain disquieting. But there is some scientific evidence to support it. One study tracked the psychological development of 3,000 children over a quarter-century. It found that psychopathic features such as charm and lying could already be detected in children as young as age three. Moreover, brain imaging has shown that the brains of adolescents who score high on the Psychopathy Checklist-Revised, which includes behaviors such as charm, lying, conning, and manipulation, contain certain abnormalities. Could such abnormalities have set them up for psychopathy at a younger age? It's a possibility.

IT DOESN'T STOP WITH DECEPTION

Unfortunately, lying, charm, conning, and manipulation aren't the only behaviors signaling depravity. Here is an overview of some others.

A failure to take responsibility. This is common among antisocial and psychopathic adults. This roster includes job slackers, debt defaulters, and deadbeat dads. Youth can also be headed in this direction, a study by Drew Westen, PhD, an Emory University psychologist, and colleagues found. Westen and his team asked some 300 mental health professionals to send them a description of a teen patient they had had at some point who had shown a maladaptive personality. Westen and his coworkers analyzed the descriptions of these teens and found that they displayed pretty much the same personality disorders that adults do, including antisocial personality disorder and psychopathy. And one of the behaviors that antisocial and psychopathic youth displayed was irresponsibility.

A lack of empathy. One of the behaviors that characterizes psychopathy is a lack of empathy. This behavior, like lying, charm, conning, and manipulation, can start at a surprisingly early age, according to a study reported by Carolyn Zahn-Waxler, PhD, of the University of Wisconsin and colleagues in the February 2013 *Journal of Child Psychology and Psychiatry.*

The researchers recruited some 1,000 children 14 to 36 months of age for their study, evaluated them for empathy, then followed them up to age 17 to see which ones engaged in antisocial behaviors. Disregard for others in toddlerhood or early childhood strongly predicted antisocial behavior later.

Antisocial or psychopathic individuals don't always lack empathy, though, Glen Gabbard, MD, alerts us. Sometimes they use it to exploit others. Gabbard reports a disconcerting case where that actually happened.

A man, whom we'll call Harry, entered a hospital emergency room, claiming that he was seriously depressed because his wife had died recently in a car accident. The psychiatry resident on duty in the emergency room asked him various questions to learn more about his situation. One was whether he and his wife had had a good sex life. "My wife and I didn't have sex," he tartly replied. "We made love!" Eventually Harry's answers convinced the resident that he had passionately loved his wife, was keenly depressed by her death, and even in danger of taking his own life because of it, and she decided to admit him to the hospital's psychiatry ward. Once he was on the ward, however, it soon became apparent that he really wasn't suicidal, and he was released. Only later did the resident learn, to her dismay, that he had used his hours on the ward to chat up other patients and convince them to buy nonexistent land in Florida from him.

"He tuned in perfectly to what would soften me up and get me to admit him to the ward!" she lamented.

A need for control. A need for control is another indicator that somebody is up to no good and capable of hurting you. Consider the following true story.

Debra Davis, a young Houston woman, didn't have a very happy past. She had been sexually molested at age six; had gotten pregnant at age 17; and, although marrying the father of her child, had divorced him at age 26. However, when she met a 38-year-old ex-Marine at a nightclub named Robert Ben "Dusty" Rhoades, life seemed to be looking up.

Dusty was pleasant company, an excellent listener. He took Debra out for a romantic candlelight dinner, then later made passionate love to her. He even invited Debra and her three children to move in with him. They all got on fine—at first. But then a less-alluring Dusty started to emerge.

When he and Debra went out together, he insisted that she dress exactly as he wanted. He took her to a swinger club. She didn't like the idea but decided to give it a try. He attempted to introduce some sadomasochistic devices into their sex life. And when he demanded anal sex and Debra refused, he raped her.

Debra got the message. She packed her bags, grabbed her children, and fled the house—none too soon. Dusty Rhoades, she eventually learned, was a sadistic sex killer.

A desire for control, in fact, is sometimes the reason why people get angry, Henri Parens, MD, a Philadelphia psychiatrist-psychoanalyst, has determined. And anger – no surprise! – can be a bellwether for danger.

University of Pennsylvania investigators analyzed data regarding 95 people serving prison sentences for murder. Rage, mostly directed at a partner or a family member, had been the chief motive for their acts. And Westen and his colleagues found that intense anger, out of proportion to the situation, is common to antisocial or psychopathic teens. The smallest provocation can fire them into a fury, where they break things or assault somebody. Incensed adults can be just as hazardous: Think road ragers and domestic abusers.

Animal torture One of the most disturbing experiences of my childhood, which I mentioned in the preface to this book, was coming across two boys plucking legs off a grasshopper one by one.

Their glee was apparent; it turned my stomach. Even today it makes me feel queasy. What became of the two boys? I don't know. Maybe it's good that I don't.

Animal torture is often a rehearsal for torturing and killing people, forensic experts have learned. Thus, youth who engage in it are not just antisocial and psychopathic, but sadistic, and may very well be headed for evildoing big time.

For instance, during their childhood, serial sex killers David Berkowitz and Edmund Kemper had tortured and killed animals. One of Berkowitz's earliest victims was his mother's parakeet. He stealthily fed it cleaning powder over a number of weeks until it finally died. Kemper buried a kitten alive, dug it up, took it to his room, decapitated it, put its head on a spindle, then mockingly paid homage to it.

Being a loner. On April 16, 2007—nearly eight years to the day after Eric Harris and Dylan Klebold killed 12 students and a teacher at Columbine High School—a student at Virginia Tech University in Blacksburg, Virginia gunned down 32 students before killing himself.

The slayer was Seung-Hui Cho, a senior at Virginia Tech. He had been a loner.

Certainly not all people who shy away from others are potential evildoers. They may suffer from social anxiety. Or maybe they are on the autism spectrum. Nonetheless, being a loner—or what psychiatrists describe as having a schizoid personality—can be a sign of a deeply troubled individual who may have it in for others, including you and your loved ones.

J. Reid Meloy, PhD, of the University of California, San Diego and his colleagues scrutinized the psychiatric histories of 34 adolescent mass murderers to get some idea of who they were and how we might possibly shield ourselves from such individuals. Almost half had been bullied by others, preoccupied with violent fantasies, and had engaged in violent acts. The majority had been loners.

Adult mass murderers also tend to engage in odd and reclusive behaviors, Robert I. Simon, MD, a forensic psychiatrist affiliated with Georgetown University, tells us. They might look like the guy next door, but are often solitary creatures, drifting from job to job or from city to city.

Serial killers likewise tend to go it alone, evildoer expert Michael Stone, MD, reports. "What is most remarkable about serial killers as a group is the extreme over-representation of [the] schizoid personality," he has written. "Whereas this disorder is found only in approximately one percent of the general population, it is exhibited in nearly half the serial killers [I have studied]."

Destroying property. When children engage in fire-setting, particularly in combination with cruelty to animals and bed-wetting, it may be a sign that they are headed toward an adulthood of depravity. A prime example was a Watertown, New York resident named Arthur Shawcross.

As a child, Shawcross was obviously troubled. In addition to engaging in fire-setting, animal torture, and bed-wetting, he bullied classmates and insulted teachers. Still, he achieved top grades, excelled in sports and, after graduation, served in the armed forces in Vietnam.

Upon returning home to Watertown, though, he committed arsons and burglaries. He was caught, tried, convicted, imprisoned for two years, then paroled in the care of his parents. After that, he strangled a boy and a girl. Back to prison he went for those murders.

Yet he was a model prisoner and paroled once more. This time he turned to stalking, sexually assaulting, and murdering prostitutes.

Again he was caught, tried, convicted, and, thankfully, sentenced to life imprisonment without the possibility of parole.

Arson, of course, is not the only kind of property damage that individuals with bad intentions engage in and that could impact you in your everyday life. I know an adolescent who was apprehended after breaking into a warehouse and destroying goods there. The police asked him why he had done it. He said that he missed his father, who had died several years earlier. I also know a man who, after the suicide of his wife, took his rage out by rear-ending several drivers and by driving into the bushes belonging to his neighbors. The neighbors were relieved when he sold his pricey waterfront home and moved on.

Narcissism. In the German Historical Museum in Berlin, you can view a gigantic wooden desk displayed behind a protective wall of glass. It obviously belonged to an outsized personality with an outsized ego. Can you guess who it was? Yes, Adolf Hitler—one of the most despicable individuals the world has known and a narcissist of the first order.

Narcissists are people who have an exaggerated sense of their own self-importance. They tend to feel entitled and to disregard the needs and feelings of others. Surely many Americans would consider President Donald Trump a narcissist in view of the salvo of insensitive, insulting tweets he shoots at various people. I asked a highly successful businessman who had voted for Trump what he thought of Trump two years into Trump's presidency. He said that he liked Trump's pragmatic, get-things-done style. Still, he admitted, "Trump is not a nice person. I wouldn't want him for a friend."

You can find narcissists in places other than the Oval Office, of course. I know a few personally but won't name names!

Since narcissism is a common characteristic of psychopathic-antisocial individuals, some narcissists can be incredibly treacherous. A study of people who attempted to approach the Royal Family in Britain in abnormal or inappropriate ways found that it was the personality trait of grandiosity that made some of them dangerous to the Royal Family. In the opinion of Joseph Merlino, MD, a clinical professor of psychiatry at New York University, narcissists are the most noxious individuals in the workplace because their sense of entitlement and disregard for others can make them ruthless. Think: Sexual harassment and all the villains swept up in the 2017 Me Too Movement!

Physical abuse. Although women often fear being murdered by a stranger on the streets, they are more likely to be killed by a spouse, lover, ex-spouse, or ex-lover. And one of the major factors increasing women's chances of being done in by a partner or ex-partner is having been physically abused by him, Jacqueline Campbell, PhD, a professor of nursing at Johns Hopkins University, and her colleagues reported in the July 2003 *American Journal of Public Health*.

Practical jokes. Although practical jokes may amuse the perpetrators, they may not amuse the victims, University of Alabama psychiatrist Charles Ford, MD, writes in his book about deceit. The reason why, he says, is that practical jokes often mask aggression and hostility in the guise of good clean fun. Consider the following story about an Indianapolis couple, Mike and Dorothy Sherrill.

In 1986, the Sherrills endured an excruciating experience when their six-year-old daughter Shannon disappeared from their front yard and was never seen again. Presumably somebody had abducted her. You can only imagine their joy when, 17 years later, a woman called them, as well as law-enforcement officers, claiming to be Shannon. Alas, it turned out to be a cruel hoax played by a Topeka, Kansas woman named Donna Walker. Walker was already known to the FBI for churning out fabricated stories.

Rejection. None of us likes being excluded or not accepted. I still recall how my mother broke into tears recalling something that had happened back during her college days. She and one other student made it to the final selection by a sorority, but it was the other student, not her, who was chosen.

And when rejection comes from somebody close to you, the pain can be even more searing. Examples: Men who leave their wives for another woman or women who walk out on their husbands without having the courtesy of telling them why. I know of two such cases.

When people close to you reject you, are they evildoers? Maybe, depending on their motive and how they handle the situation. Say, a friend suddenly turns cold without explaining why. "It's more than just pulling away," Jan Yager, PhD, a University of Connecticut sociologist, argues in her book *When Friendship Hurts.* "The silent treatment is actually malicious."

Verbal abuse. When a person says something that hurts another, the comment may have been made thoughtlessly, without realizing its potential toxicity. And in such cases, the person certainly bears some responsibility for the wrong he or she has exacted. But there are individuals who purposefully say things to hurt others; and they, I would argue, are evildoers big time.

When people intentionally say things that put others down, it is often done to put themselves up. For instance, they might say, "I don't want to upset you, but…" (They probably do.) They might say, "I hope this doesn't insult you, but…" (Here comes an insult.) If you are sick, they might sneer in the presence of a colleague, making sure you overhear, "She's always sick!"

Sometimes verbal abusers use body language rather than words to shoot quivers into their victims. It could be the cocking of an eyebrow, a roll of the eyeballs, or simply a frown.

Like rejection, verbal abuse can leave lasting scars. One 32-year-old still recalls how, at age 11, a supposed friend called her a derogatory name. It so devastated her that ever since, she has had trouble opening up and trusting people.

HOW TO DEAL WITH THESE VARIOUS RED FLAGS

Are there any general take-home messages regarding these numerous red flags? Yes, I think so.

Don't Be Too Trusting. Somebody once accused me of being overly trusting of other people's good intentions. He may have been right. He certainly would have been correct if he had said it about my father, who loved people and had a big heart. One time an acquaintance came to my father with tears in his eyes, reporting that he was on the brink of financial ruin and begging my father to lend him money. My father did so—a fifth of our family income for that year. When my mother found out, she was furious. And with good reason: The man moved to California and was never heard from again.

But it's not just us regular folks who are gullible. Sometimes the experts are too. Let me tell you about a psychiatrist who, because of his excessive trust, ended up paying for it with his life.

Back in 2006, Wayne Fenton, MD, was an international expert on schizophrenia and affiliated with the National Institute of Mental Health (NIMH) in Bethesda, Maryland. He also saw psychiatric patients privately in an office located across from the NIMH, off Old Georgetown Road. He was known to be devoted to his patients, especially to those who were seriously mentally ill.

On the Sunday of Labor Day weekend, the father of a 19-year-old son with schizophrenia called Fenton and begged him to see his son in his office. The son had been experiencing delusions of persecution and was refusing to take his medications, the father said. Fenton agreed to meet them at his office. Once the father had delivered his son to Fenton, the father apparently left to do an errand. When he returned, his son was wandering outside Fenton's office with blood on his hands and clothing. The father called 911. When the paramedics arrived, they found Fenton on his office floor, severely beaten and dead.

Some other psychiatrists commented later on the tragedy. One said that while most patients with schizophrenia are not dangerous, a few are, and that psychiatrists should be extremely cautious whenever schizophrenia patients show delusions of persecution or other signs of aggression. Another said that the patient who murdered Fenton should probably have been seen in the hospital emergency room, not in a private office, where there would have been other staff to restrain him if he had become violent.

Frankly, it remains an ongoing challenge throughout life to maintain a healthy balance between trust and distrust, psychiatrist Anton Kris, MD, counsels us.

Take Threats Seriously. Carl Bell, MD, a Chicago psychiatrist, once mentioned to me that if somebody threatens you, you should take the threat in earnest. Certainly, there is ample evidence to support his advice.

Individuals who stalk and attack private citizens, often a prior sexual intimate, usually threaten verbally beforehand, J. Reid Meloy, PhD, reports.

A man named James Davis worked in a tool warehouse in Asheville, North Carolina. He once mentioned to his colleagues, "If they ever decide to fire me, I'll take two or three of them with me." His employers did eventually fire him, and he was true to his promise.

One day, while our college-age daughter was driving to school, a car in front of her braked suddenly. She rear-ended it. She got out of the car, as did the man whose car she had hit, to assess the damage. The man blamed her for the accident and demanded that she give him several hundred dollars in compensation. Suspecting that he had set her up, she refused. He then told her that he was going to sue her, which he did. Actually, he sued not just her, but my husband and myself for $10 million!

Follow Your Instincts. If you feel something isn't right, it probably isn't.

The chill of dread, a fear of predation, can be a sure sign of the presence of a malevolent personality, Glen Gabbard, MD, warns us. "I try to teach my residents to trust their gut instinct," he says. "If you think you are not safe, and you feel the hair on the back of your neck standing up, trust that instinct."

It was DNA evidence that finally led to the identification of Kansas's Bind, Torture, and Kill (BTK) serial killer Dennis Rader (detailed in the previous chapter). But long before, various people had had disturbing impressions of him that might have helped point law enforcement officials in his direction if they had reported their impressions. For instance, the couple who lived behind him found it weird that he would often photograph their house. Other neighbors had been annoyed when he accused them of violating city codes. The mother of a boy in Rader's Cub Scout group pulled him out because she found Rader's demeanor strange.

True, such minute details may seem trivial and not worth sharing with the police. But sometimes when a number of such minute details are pooled, they help law enforcement officials form a picture of an offender and lead to his identification and apprehension, Gregg McCrary of Fredericksburg, Virginia tells us. McCrary used to work for the Federal Bureau of Investigation (FBI) as a psychological profiler.

So, if you have observed somebody engaging in a disturbing behavior, or have been the target of someone's disturbing behavior, it might be appropriate to report it to the police. Or perhaps not. Many troubling behaviors are not criminal offenses. But whenever you observe, or experience, somebody doing something unacceptable, you should try to find a way to deal with it that seems appropriate to the situation.

Let's say somebody at work likes to put you down. How to handle it? In his book *Nasty People,* Jay Carter suggests a number of options. You can look at her to let her know exactly what she is doing to you by giving her a knowing smile, raising your eyebrows at her, staring at her, or squeezing her cheek. You can challenge her demeaning comment with a demeaning counter-comment: "So, you really think so?" Or you might demand that she repeat her insulting remark, then retort: "Oh, that is what I *thought* you said."

Unfortunately, action, however appropriate, doesn't always work.

Sometime before Virginia Tech student Seung-Hui Cho became a mass killer, two of his English teachers, Lucinda Roy and Nikki Giovanni, were extremely concerned about his writings for class because they were violent, profane, and contained veiled threats. Roy contacted counseling services, student affairs, officials in the English department, and the campus police. University officials said that she could drop Roy from classes where he presented offensive material. The police offered to provide security during those classes but said that they could take no further action because Cho's works contained no direct threats. The eventual result: 32 people dead.

But sometimes efforts to deal with the depraved do indeed bear fruit.

Just days after the March 2001 Santana High School shooting in Santana, California, some students in another California high school heard a handful of fellow students plotting to put a bomb on a teacher's desk and kill people. They alerted the police. The police arrested the plotters before they could carry out their nefarious plan.

In 2017, an 18-year-old named Nicole Savario was planning a mass shooting at Catoctin High School in Thurmont, Maryland. Her father found materials for making a bomb in their home. He contacted the police.

Then there was the infamous Unabomber of the 1990s who has become a popular legend. Few people know much, though, about his troubled psyche or the psychological devastation he unleashed on his family. It is a fascinating, but heart-rending story, told by Ted's brother, David Kaczynski, at a meeting of the American Psychoanalytic Association in 2008.

"I think I always knew that my brother Ted was different," David Kaczynski related. "But in a good way. He was a legend in our school system." Yet Ted also tended to have no friends, which worried both David and their parents. Then, during the 1960s, Ted decided to give up his career as a professor of mathematics at the University of California, Berkeley and to move into a Montana cabin. During the 1970s, his behavior became more disturbing. He wrote his parents a letter saying that they had never loved him. During the 1980s, David decided to marry a childhood friend and sent Ted a letter asking Ted to be his best man. "I don't think we can be brothers any longer," Ted wrote back.

After they were married, David and his wife received more bizarre letters from Ted. "You know, David," she said, "your brother is sick." She persuaded David to take some of Ted's letters to a psychiatrist. The psychiatrist examined the letters and said that Ted probably had schizophrenia. The psychiatrist and David devised ways to get Ted into treatment. Unfortunately, none of their strategies worked.

In 1995, David and his wife read articles in the press about the

Unabomber. There was reason to believe that the Unabomber had something to do with Berkeley. David's wife asked him: "Is there a chance that your brother might be the Unabomber?"

David and his wife were faced with a grim dilemma. Should they contact the police and share their suspicions? On one hand, if Ted were indeed the Unabomber, they had to stop him before he killed somebody else. On the other, if Ted were indeed the Unabomber, he would probably be given the death sentence, and they would have that on their conscience.

In 1996, David decided to turn Ted in. FBI agents found the Unabomber manifesto in Ted's cabin. There was no doubt that Ted was the Unabomber, David said.

The prosecution hired a well-known forensic psychiatrist to help them make the case that Ted should get the death penalty. Defense psychiatrists who evaluated Ted diagnosed him with paranoid schizophrenia. During 1997 and 1998, Ted went on trial. The prosecutor offered a plea bargain that would spare Ted's life. Today, Ted is serving a life sentence without the possibility of parole.

TWELVE

HOW TO PROTECT YOURSELF AND YOUR LOVED ONES FROM BULLYING

Remember the film *A Christmas Story?* And remember the scene where the neighborhood bully Scut Farkus—with a rancid coonskin cap shoved down over his red hair, his serpentine yellow eyes narrowed into slits, and his mouth pulled back into a snarl—lunges at the hero, nine-year-old Ralphie Parker? Eventually Ralphie snaps and beats Scut up. Bully problem solved. The good guy wins.

Alas, if real-life bullying were always limited to minor neighborhood scrapes and always solved so easily! Bullying, as we'll see, is a much more widespread and complex societal problem, often with grave consequences and no easy solutions.

Whenever an individual is intentionally mean to another person, he or she is an evildoer. And whenever he or she derives pleasure from the act, he or she is a sadist as well. A bully is often both. But to be a bully, a person must meet still a third criterion: He or she must repeatedly dish out cruelty to a victim.

Why do people bully? Generally to achieve power and control over a victim. Such a motive certainly appears to drive a large number of bullies, Michael Craig Miller, MD, a Harvard Medical School psychiatrist with a special interest in bullying, told me. Put simply, they put others down to put themselves up. They need to win.

But why this lust for power and control? Narcissism appears to be a major reason, according to Lynne Curry, PhD, a workplace bullying expert and workplace coach in Anchorage, Alaska. Narcissistic bullies believe they are superior to others, enjoy talking about themselves, crave the limelight, don't like it when others receive attention or praise, and can't take criticism. And, oh yes, they often have an entourage of sycophants (toadies) who stroke their egos.

Still other bullies hunger after power and control because of envy. For instance, there is a type of bullying teacher that seems to be envious of bright children and to put them down for that reason, one bullying expert noted.

A lust for power and control doesn't power all cases of bullying, though. Sometimes, Miller said, people harass others to obtain money or sex, or they put others down who remind them of aspects of themselves which they don't like.

WHAT? BULLIES IN THE PLAYPEN?

Henri Parens, MD, is a Philadelphia psychoanalyst. A few years ago, he sat down in the posh Waldorf Astoria Hotel in New York City with some like-minded psychoanalysts to analyze the phenomenon of human aggression.

There seem to be two kinds of aggression, Parens ventured. One is a healthy kind such as trying to solve a math problem. In fact, a moderate amount of aggression may be beneficial to people's immune systems. The other is an unhealthy kind such as expressions of hostility. And this latter sort can unfortunately start very early in life. "I have seen 12-month-olds already bullying and teasing each other," Parens reported. "I couldn't believe it!"

But yes, bullies in the playpen. So, it looks as if bullies can't start too early flexing their bullying muscles.

And you won't believe the number of other places where, as they grow, and where, as their bullying tactics improve, bullies will loom large.

You can find bullies in the schoolyard and neighborhood, of course, but also in school buses, school hallways, school locker rooms, school cafeterias, and even school classrooms. Nor are homes necessarily safe havens from bullies: There you may find them in the guise of sibling torturers or domestic abusers. And interestingly, some of yesterday's school bullies have morphed into today's domestic abusers. This finding comes from a study headed by Kathyrn Falb, a doctoral student at the Harvard School of Public Health.

And don't necessarily expect to escape bullies in the workplace. There you may encounter bullying bosses and bullying coworkers. Moreover, there are bullying doctors, bullying lawyers, bullying teachers, bullying police, bullying journalists, and even bullying clergy. I once overheard a minister admit to, during his youth, of having called a boy "a fag." "It was horrible what I did," he confessed. "It probably scarred him for life."

There are even institutional bullies, psychiatrist James Maier, MD reminds us. In the world of psychiatry, for instance, licensing boards, insurance companies, and even medical centers have been known to beat up on psychiatrists to get their way, Maier reports.

Also disconcerting: Bullies are incredibly common, at least in the United States. The National Institute for Occupational Safety and Health surveyed employees at more than 500 organizations to learn how many had been victims of workplace bullying. Twenty-five percent reported that they had. An international study found that 25 percent of youth in the United States had had experience with bullying either as victim, bully, or both, compared with 11 percent on average for youth in other countries.

SO BULLIES ARE EVERYWHERE: BUT WHOM DO THEY TARGET?

When it comes to schoolyard bullying, bullies tend to pick on smaller or weaker children. But as children grow older, bullies often set their sights on those individuals who are withdrawn, unassertive, or easily upset. Or they may target particular minority groups.

For instance, sexual orientation and gender identification are two of the top reasons why American youth are bullied, according to the Sex Information and Education Council of the United States. By the eighth grade, two thirds of gifted pupils have already been singled out by bullies, two Purdue University researchers, Jean Peterson, PhD, an associate professor of educational studies, and Karen Ray, a doctoral student in counseling psychology, have found.

In the workplace, bully bosses are just as likely to go after strong subordinates as weak ones, Gary Namie, PhD, director of the Workplace Bullying and Trauma Institute in Bellingham, Washington, reports. The reason? Perhaps because it's just as much fun to flex their bully muscles with those higher up the food chain as with those down below. Actually pleasure in exerting power is the major reason why bully bosses bully their employees, Harvey Hornstein, PhD, a retired professor from Columbia University Teachers College, told *The New York Times.* It's "a kind of low-grade sadism," he says.

And let's face it: If many or most cases of bullying involve sadism, no wonder bullies use an array of tools to torture their victims.

The tools may be verbal. For instance, the bully may belittle, berate, defame, gossip, humiliate, make ethnic or racial slurs, make false accusations, taunt, tease, or threaten.

The tools may be physical, for example, hitting, kicking, or shoving.

The tools may consist of other actions: blocking a promotion, dropping a friend, excluding somebody from your group, failing to return phone calls, glaring, giving a bad reference, intimidating, or sabotaging.

Sometimes the tools are as inventive as they are cruel. Here are a few examples: creating a Web site that contains cartoons, pictures, or jokes ridiculing others; taking a picture of someone in the locker room, then sending it to others; adding a person's face to a pornographic image online; tricking somebody into divulging sensitive personal information in an e-mail, then forwarding the information to others. And in China, where school bullying has become an increasingly pressing problem, a few bullies have resorted to such vile measures as making victims drink urine or threatening them with arsenic poisoning.

And how about the command "Drink bleach and die!"? A coterie of girls in Lakeland, Florida purportedly sent this cyber message, among others, to 12-year-old Rebecca Sedwick, urging her to kill herself. Pretty ghastly, don't you think?

THE IMPACT CAN BE PROFOUND

Yet also pretty effective. Although Rebecca did not respond to that particular command, she did jump to her death at an abandoned cement plant in September 2013.

Fortunately, most cases of youth bullying don't end up so tragically. Nonetheless, they can inflict extensive, sometimes profound mental damage.

For example, being picked on by a brother or sister while growing up may seem like pretty routine stuff. But for some youngsters, the harassment can provoke anxiety and depression, Corinna Jenkins Tucker, PhD, an associate professor of family studies at the University of New Hampshire, found in an investigation. Thus parents should not turn a blind eye when their children taunt, tease, or beat each other up, Tucker advises.

Purdue University researchers Peterson and Ray found that bullying can trigger depression, unexpressed rage, and school absenteeism in gifted students. "All children are affected adversely by bullying, but gifted children differ from other children in significant ways," Peterson told the Purdue News Service. "Many are intense, sensitive, and stressed by their own and others' high expectations, and their ability, interests, and behavior may make them vulnerable. Additionally, social justice issues are very important to them, and they struggle to make sense of cruelty and aggression. Perfectionists may become even more self-critical, trying to avoid mistakes that might draw attention to themselves."

In 2002, the American Medical Association issued a landmark report regarding bullying among American youth. Bullying often leads to anxiety and depressive disorders, and the problem deserves attention by American physicians, the report urged.

School bullying can unleash somatic illnesses as well, Stuart Twemlow, MD, a professor of psychiatry at Baylor College of Medicine, tells us. Twemlow should know: He grew up on the rough side of a town in New Zealand, developed a passion for defending the underdog, and is today an international school bullying expert.

In one of his studies, Twemlow and his colleagues studied 590 children in grades 3 through 5 from six public elementary schools in the Midwest. During the fall semester, cases of bully victimization and cases of bully aggression were identified – the former via self report and the latter via peer report. School nursing logs were also examined to learn how often each child visited the school nurse during the fall semester because of a somatic complaint, illness, or injury. The average number was five. The researchers then looked to see whether instances of being victimized by a bully or instances of doing the bullying were significantly related to school-nurse visits, controlling for demographic variables.

The researchers found that such a relationship did in fact exist. Involvement in bullying—whether as bully, victim, or both—was associated with increased somatic illnesses and injury complaints to the school nurse. The reason? Maybe because being chronically stressed weakens a person's immune system.

Interestingly, similar results emerged from an international bullying study headed by Tonja Nansel, PhD, an investigator at the National Institute of Child Health and Human Development in Bethesda, Maryland. Youths involved in bullying – as bully, victim, or both – reported not just markedly poorer emotional and school adjustment, but also notably higher levels of health problems than did non-involved youth in nearly all the countries surveyed. Health problems included headaches, stomachaches, backaches, irritability, nervousness, dizziness, and sleep difficulties.

Moreover, the corrosive impact of being bullied in childhood can persist into early adulthood, a study by William Copeland, PhD, an associate professor of psychiatry at Duke University, has shown.

The investigation included some 1,400 subjects who were evaluated periodically during childhood, adolescence, and young adulthood as far as school bullying and psychiatric disorders were concerned. Five percent of the subjects were found to be bullies, 22 percent bully victims, 5 percent both bullies and victims, and the remaining 68 percent unaffected by bullying. The researchers looked to see, after taking childhood hardship or childhood psychiatric disorders into consideration, whether bullies, victims, or bullies/victims were more prone to psychiatric disorders as young adults than were those subjects who had been unaffected by it (the controls).

As it turned out, the answer was yes for all three groups. Compared to controls, those who had been bullies were four times more likely to have antisocial personality disorder. Compared to controls, those who had been victims were five times more likely to have agoraphobia (fear of open spaces), three times more likely to have generalized anxiety disorder, and three times more likely to have panic disorder. And compared to controls, those who had been both bullies and victims were five times more likely to have depression, 15 times more likely to have panic disorder, and in the case of males, 19 times more likely to be suicidal.

The noxious impact of being bullied while young can even extend into middle age, a five decade-long study conducted by researchers at the Institute of Psychiatry, King's College, London shows. Subjects hailed not just from England, but from Scotland and Wales. Subjects who had been bullied frequently as children experienced higher rates of anxiety and suicidal thoughts or plans at age 45 than did those who had been spared childhood bullying. They were also less likely to be living with a partner, were more isolated, and had lower levels of life satisfaction than did the latter. Even those who had been bullied only occasionally were more likely than those who had not been to experience depression, poorer cognitive functioning, and poorer general health.

Nor are the long-range deleterious effects of bullying limited to the United Kingdom. You can also find them in the "Middle Kingdom"—a nickname for China. One Chinese woman reported on the Internet that her adolescent classmates had ridiculed and humiliated her because she had body odor. "All I thought about in those years was killing myself and killing those who humiliated me," she confessed. "I hated to hang out with people, quit school, and suffered depression. Even now, I still have social phobias, a fear of other people's attention, and I do not easily trust others."

And if the long-range injurious psychological fallout isn't enough, being bullied in childhood can lead to destructive behaviors such as drug use, shoplifting, vandalism, and violence, research has shown.

For instance, researchers at the National Institute of Child Health and Human Development in Bethesda, Maryland evaluated the frequency of weapon carrying and fighting in a large cohort of both 10th grade bullies and 10th grade bully victims. Although the bullies were more likely to carry weapons and fight than the bully victims were, the latter were also often likely to do so.

In another study, headed by Sara Goldstein, PhD, an assistant professor of family and child studies at Montclair State University in New Jersey, some 1,300 adolescents and teens were examined regarding the frequency and impact of being relationally bullied. Relational bullying was defined as socially manipulative behavior intended to hurt others, such as spreading rumors about them, dropping them as a friend, or excluding them from the group. Sixty-one percent of the girls and 52 percent of the boys had experienced relational bullying, Goldstein and her coworkers found. Having been relationally bullied was significantly linked with feeling less positive about social experiences at school. This was true for students of both genders. Furthermore, having been relationally bullied was significantly linked in boys (although not in girls) with carrying a weapon to school.

One of the most unsettling findings of their study, Perdue University researchers Peterson and Ray contend, is that 11 percent of the gifted students who had been bullied reported that they had responded to the bullying with violence.

Arguably, the most pernicious behavioral outcome of being

bullied in childhood is deciding to take revenge for it through an act of mass violence.

In 1999, for instance, two teens—Eric Harris and Dylan Klebold—stormed into Columbine High School in Columbine, Colorado, killing 12 students, a teacher, and finally themselves. Both teens had been bullied by classmates.

In 2001, 15-year-old Charles "Andy" Williams of Santee, California opened gunfire on his high school classmates, killing two and wounding 13. Williams, a small, hunched-over boy with elfin ears and doe-like eyes, had also been bullied. "He'd be walking down the hallway, and people would come up and punch him in the back of the head," a friend from where he was originally from (rural Maryland) later recalled. They would also shove him, humiliate him, and knock him down, Santee high school classmates later testified. "I can't take it anymore, I can't take being treated like this," he had told his Maryland friend.

And you might recall Timothy McVeigh, the Oklahoma City Bomber. He had been shy and withdrawn in school and the target of bullying. He took refuge in a fantasy world where he imagined retaliating against the bullies. Eventually, the youth who had bullied him were replaced in his mind by the ultimate bully, the United States Government. In 1995, he bombed a federal government building in Oklahoma City, killing 168 people and injuring at least 680 others.

MCVEIGH GONE, BUT WORKPLACE STILL ENDANGERED

McVeigh received the death sentence for his domestic terrorism act and was executed on June 11, 2001. But unfortunately, America's workplaces are still not safe from the toxic impact of bullying. The dangers may lurk without, or they may lurk within, but either way, the mental and physical consequences can be injurious, if not deadly.

A few years ago, Italian psychiatrist Renato Gilioli, MD, of the University of Milan set up the first center in Italy devoted to helping people afflicted by workplace-related mental illness Subsequently they learned that almost 60 percent of their patients were the victims of workplace bullying, and as a consequence, were suffering from adjustment difficulties, anxiety, depression, exhaustion, sexual impairment, difficulty falling asleep, or nightmares about their situations at work.

Researchers at the University of Manitoba in Canada found that the emotional toll of workplace bullying is even more severe than that of sexual harassment.

Furthermore, people bullied in the workplace may abuse alcohol or other substances to cope with their distress, Judith Richman, PhD, a professor of psychiatry at the University of Illinois at Chicago, found in a study of some 2,500 university employees.

And even those professionals whom you think might be more inured to the harmful impact of workplace bullying may not necessarily be so. Take the case of psychiatrists, who have learned what makes people tick and how to deal with them. Nonetheless, a survey of 60 psychiatrists found that 57 out of the 60 had been targeted by workplace bullying at some point in their careers, and of those 57 who had been targeted, 82 percent had been distressed by it to some degree —40 percent moderately, 30 percent mildly, and 12 percent severely.

In brief: Bullying can erode the minds, hearts, and souls of virtually all of us.

TAKING ON THE BULLY

So, a bully currently has you—or your child—in his or her sights. What to do about it?

First off, *do not* make a knee-jerk response, but rather control your breathing and weigh possible recourses. So advises Alaska work-place bullying expert Lynne Curry, PhD.

Then ask yourself: Should I respond? If it's a trivial issue, probably not, Curry says. Two youth bullying experts, Sameer Hinduja, PhD, a professor of criminology at Florida Atlantic University, and Justin Patchin, PhD, a professor of criminal justice at the University of Wisconsin-Eau Claire, concur. The most effective response to minor forms of cyberbullying is no response at all, they contend, because this way, you give the bully no satisfaction in having raised your hackles.

Yet if the bully attack is more than trivial, you should probably take action. Then the question is: How?

Fleeing the scene appears to be a good choice in a number of instances.

Erika Harold, the 2003 Miss America, is African American, Cherokee Indian, and white. Back when she was in the ninth grade, she endured racial and ethnic slurs, property vandalism, and even death threats. She eventually changed to another school that was more diverse.

A teen I know, who is sensitive and highly artistic, used to be bullied in school. For instance, when she sat down in the school cafeteria for lunch, the other girls would move away from her. She then switched to a school that accepts only students who have art talent and are serious about a career in that area. Everybody in her new school treats her great, she happily reports.

If you're being bullied at work, looking for a position in another organization is often the best solution, Lisa Gold, MD, a clinical associate professor of psychiatry at Georgetown University, recommends. The reason why, she explains, is that if bullying is occurring in your workplace, "there is a culture there that tolerates it," and it is highly unlikely that such a culture can be detoxified.

But suppose fleeing the bully would be hard or impossible. What should you or your child do then? Let's take a look at school bullying first.

"Most [school] bullies are psychopathic, which makes it hard for them to empathize," school bullying expert Stuart Twemlow, MD, reports. "Yet punishing bullies is not the answer to bullying. There is a video game called 'Bullying' where you can beat the bully up. That's not good."

In contrast, taking a course in martial arts to defend yourself in case a bully jumps you might be a wise move, he indicates. And perhaps even better, is obtaining the help of those "many students who do not bully, but who get a buzz out of watching someone else do it" and especially obtaining the help of youngsters who don't like it and who could serve as natural leaders. Indeed, in his efforts to reduce bullying in schools, Twemlow attempts to recruit such bystanders to help in dispute mediation between the bully and bully victim, and more often than not they are happy to assist, he says.

Now, how to deal with workplace bullying? Confronting a coworker bully or retaliating can be risky tactics, Loraleigh Keashly, PhD, an expert on the subject at Wayne State University in Detroit, reports. The reason why? Your employer might view you, not the bully, as the problem. Workplace bully expert Lynne Curry agrees: Don't let a bully push you into being less than you are.

A safer, and sometimes more fruitful move, Keashly says, is going to your boss and discussing the problem or finding out whether your coworkers are also being bullied, and if so, perhaps forming an alliance with them. For instance, Keashly once consulted on a case where one teacher bullied other teachers until one of the victims decided to not take it anymore. She talked various colleagues into joining her in reporting the bully to the principal.

Dealing with a bully boss can be still more challenging. But even if you hate conflict and tend to be a marshmallow, standing up to him (or her) may be an effective solution, workplace bullying expert Lynne Curry, PhD, reports. Here's how you can go about it, she says.

Let's say your boss demands: "Do this immediately!" Take a deep breath and reply calmly, "I'll get it done." If he insists "I need it now!" then say "I'll get to your project as quickly as I can." By calmly replying and resisting his demands a bit, you gain his respect and also feel better about yourself. Moreover, standing up to him the first time is usually the hardest; after that it gets easier, she assures us.

And how to deal with cyberspace bullying? That's a totally different ballgame.

CYBERSPACE BULLIES CALL FOR OTHER TACTICS

If a workplace bully harassed you in cyberspace, there is a fairly easy solution, Curry tells us. You can save, then report the posts to your social media provider, and the provider can then take action against the bully for violating its abuse policy. Some social media providers, such as Instagram, Facebook, Twitter, and YouTube, have online mechanisms for reporting abusive posts.

Yet if your child is being cyberbullied, other defense tactics are probably in order. You might talk with a trusted teacher or school counselor about the problem, Hinduja and Patchin propose. Or you might suggest to your child that she stop using her social media and e-mail accounts for a while or perhaps even close them and open new accounts. But the best way to handle the situation is to sit down and discuss it with her and come up with an action plan that both she and you approve. Otherwise it may fail.

Remember cyberbully victim Rebecca Sedwick, mentioned earlier in this chapter? Her mother apparently closed her Facebook account without her approval. As a result, Rebecca surreptitiously opened several new cellphone messaging applications, which gave her enemies access to her once again. And once again she started being inundated with texts seething with hate, such as "Why are you still alive?" "You're ugly," and "Can you die please?" It was this new onslaught of nefarious messages that apparently sent her over the edge and provided the impetus for her to kill herself.

How about legal recourse against bullying? Mixed, depending on the type of bullying and the laws on the books.

For instance, only the state of California has a specific law that makes workplace bullying illegal, according to Curry. In other states, workplace bullying is only illegal if it involves physical violence or is targeted against individuals who have protected status under certain laws, say because of age, disability, or race.

Furthermore, suits brought against cyberbullies because of "intentional infliction of emotional distress" are tough to win, Hinduja and Patchin report. The reason? Such distress needs to be caused by "extreme and outrageous conduct," and there is no precise legal definition of what "extreme and outrageous" mean.

On the other hand, if anyone puts photos online to humiliate you, it may be grounds for an invasion-of-privacy lawsuit, criminologists Hinduja and Patchin point out. If someone threatens online that they are going to harm you physically or to damage your property—forms of cyberstalking—contact the police.

Which brings us, in the next chapter, to the netherworld of stalkers and how to armor ourselves against them.

THIRTEEN
HOW TO SAFEGUARD YOURSELF AND YOUR LOVED ONES FROM STALKERS

Some time ago, I attended a family reunion and was introduced to a young guy who, I later learned, had done something outrageously creative. After his girlfriend had dumped him in favor of someone else, he ordered a hearse to pull up in front of her house on her wedding day.

When I heard this story, I found it quite amusing. Since then, I've learned something about stalkers and no longer find it funny.

First off, what is stalking? According to stalking experts, it is repeated and persistent attempts to impose on another person unwanted contact or communication that induces fear or distress. Moreover, such attempts have to last at least two weeks. If they last less than two weeks, they are considered harassment, not stalking.

Although stalking is nothing new—John Wilkes Booth tracked Abraham Lincoln before killing him—it took front stage in the public consciousness in 1989 when a Los Angeles television actress named Rebecca Schaeffer was pursued and killed by a "fan." Her murder led to the first anti-stalking law in California, or anywhere in the United States, for that matter. By 1993, all 50 states and the District of Columbia had enacted some form of anti-stalking law.

Schaeffer's murder also stepped up stalking research, which had already been quite productive.

Stalkers are mostly male, studies have divulged, and on average 37 years of age, although stalkers as young as 11 and as old as 87 years of age have been identified.

Who is targeted by stalkers? Mostly females, studies have found, especially those ages 18 to 35, to a lesser degree those ages 36 to 55, and to the least degree those 56 years of age or older. However, males can also be the target of stalkers. Again, those ages 18 to 35 are most likely to be targeted, those ages 36 to 55 less so, and those aged 56 and older least so.

Male stalkers are likely to set their sights on a broad range of victims – prior intimate partners, professionals, acquaintances, or strangers. A few years ago, while walking from the subway station to my apartment, a young woman sidled up to me and whispered, "Can I walk with you? A man is following me." "Sure," I said, and invited her to take refuge in the lobby of my apartment building until she felt that it was safe to venture out. I presumed that she was being followed by a stranger, although I never did learn for sure.

Female stalkers, in contrast, tend to focus on those with whom they have had professional contact, especially psychiatrists, psychologists, and family physicians, although teachers and legal professionals are occasionally targets.

Some 10 percent of Americans have been stalked at some point in their lives. The percent of Germans having been stalked appears to be similar—about 12 percent—according to a study headed by Harald Dressing, MD, of the Central Institute of Mental Health in Mannheim, Germany. The study was a community study carried out in the city of Mannheim.

GRANDIOSITY: A MAJOR ENGINE BEHIND STALKING

What propels stalkers to pursue their prey? Ah, that's where it gets really interesting.

David James, MD, a forensic psychiatrist with the North London Forensic Service, and colleagues studied individuals who had tracked the British royal family and found that many had symptoms of the serious mental illness schizophrenia, such as hearing voices, seeing things that really weren't there, confused thoughts, rambling speech, and delusions (false beliefs). For instance, regarding their delusions, they may have believed themselves to be members of the royal family or persecuted by it. But many of the stalkers also exhibited grandiosity.

Grandiosity is a conviction that one is hot stuff when one is not. In many cases, grandiose fantasies compensate for real-life failures in both work and love. In a sense, grandiosity is a delusion. But it appears to be more of a personality trait than the result of serious mental illness and one facet of narcissistic personality disorder.

In any event, grandiosity, like delusions due to serious mental illness, can shape stalkers' stalking agendas in myriad ways.

For instance, the study of individuals who had pursued members of the British royal family disclosed that many had sought friendship or romance with the Royals, others justice, still others protection from imagined persecutors, and that a few had been eager to offer the Royals advice.

Scrutiny of individuals who chased after Hollywood celebrities or members of Congress also unearthed a swath of motives: yearning for romance, an eagerness to sell entertainment products, a desire to shame the actor or actress for his or her sexual activity, hope for protection from a perceived persecutor, hate.

Presidential assassins have often been spurred by political

motives, J. Reid Meloy, PhD, a stalking expert in San Diego, California tells us. An example: John Wilkes Booth, Abraham Lincoln's killer. This isn't always the case, though. Lee Harvey Oswald, John Kennedy's assassin, hungered for attention, recognition, status. John Hinckley, Jr, tried to kill Ronald Reagan because he scorned society and wanted to publicize his contempt for it.

In the stalking study headed by Harold Dressing, MD, the most common motives turned out to be a desire for a loving relationship, eagerness to resume a former relationship, jealousy, or revenge.

Paul Mullen, DSc, a professor of forensic psychiatry at Monash University in Victoria, Australia, studied 145 stalkers, then classified them into five categories: the rejected, the intimacy seeker, the incompetent suitor, the resentful, and the predatory.

"Stalkers rejected by their spouses or lovers tend to vacillate between seeking reconciliation and revenge," Mullen reports. "What sustains them is narcissistic entitlement and the belief that this is the only relationship they are going to have, which they may be right about."

Intimacy seekers want to establish a relationship with their "true love" regardless of that individual's wishes. They may be prone to jealousy or become enraged when their true love ignores their attention, Mullen says.

Incompetent suitors are men who have been rebuffed in their attempts to obtain a wife or lover. "They tend to be socially inept," Mullen explains. "When they are rejected, they begin to stalk due to irritation, arrogance, and optimism that their behavior will change the woman's mind."

Resentful stalkers believe that they have been humiliated or treated unfairly by somebody and track the individual to express their rage. "They are sustained by an enormous sense of power and control over the victim," Mullen notes.

And as for predatory stalkers, they select a victim at random to attack sexually, then savor the planning and anticipation of the assault.

Mullen, along with other Australian colleagues, also conducted what appeared to be the first extensive study of juvenile stalkers. The investigation included some 300 youth whom the researchers deemed stalkers—that is, the youth engaged in unwanted intrusions into a victim's life for at least two weeks, and not only on the school grounds but in other locations as well. The subjects' most common reason for stalking, the researchers learned, was to torment their victims, followed by retaliation over rejection, a desire to impose unwanted sexual contact, and finally romantic infatuation.

Regardless of motive, stalkers' fantasies are deeply rooted and nearly intransigent, Robert T.M. Phillips, MD, PhD, a forensic psychiatrist and an adjunct associate professor of psychiatry at the University of Maryland, tells us. Phillips also serves as a consultant for the Protective Intelligence Division of the United States Secret Service.

FINDING A BULLET ON YOUR PILLOW

Although some of the communication methods that stalkers use are quite prosaic—phone calls, e-mails, text messages, approaching the victim physically, loitering near the victim's home—others are much more imaginative and often chilling, intended to scare the victim and let him know that the hunter is moving in for a kill.

For instance, a young man who was being tracked by his former fiancée arrived home to find that she had damaged his sports car. Another found obscene messages scribbled by his pursuer on his fence. A lawyer came home to find a bullet on his pillow. Another lawyer, who was prosecuting a physician, found a stethoscope lying in his driveway. And one woman, as I reported at the start of this chapter, found a hearse parked in front of her door on her wedding day. It can't get any more gruesome than that, right? Well, maybe. One stalker staked out a female entertainer's home and noticed that there were cats in her yard. It gave him the bright idea of killing a mountain lion, skinning it, having it made into a rug, then mailing it to the entertainer with this note: "I shot this because it was beautiful like you."

Also unnerving: Stalkers can be incredibly persistent.

Upon arrival in Washington, DC's Dulles Airport, a woman called the United States Secret Service, claiming that a particular member of Congress was her boyfriend and complaining that he wasn't there to meet her. She then took a taxi to his home, and since no one answered the door, pried open a window and climbed into the house. An alarm went off. When the police arrived, she told them that her boyfriend had given her permission to use his house until he arrived. The police didn't buy the story, arrested her, and charged her with unlawful entry. Nonetheless, two years later, she again flew to Washington and again tried to make contact with the same Congressman. Again without success. Ten years later, she was still writing him, phoning him, or trying to visit him.

One stalker tracked his prey for up to 40 years, stalking expert Paul Mullen says. Talk about obsessed!

THE IMPACT CAN BE DEVASTATING

You can only imagine the baleful impact that such long-term stalking could have on a person. But even shorter stalking exposure can be ruinous.

In a 2002 stalking investigation, over half of the victims evaluated were found to exhibit anger, anxiety, depression, irritation, and/or nervousness as a result of their experience. In one of Mullen's stalking studies, 83 percent of the victims were found to have experienced, as a result of their trauma, an anxiety disorder; 55 percent post-traumatic stress disorder (PTSD) or symptoms thereof such as nightmares and flashbacks; and 24 percent suicidal ideation. In Dressing's study in Germany, stalking-victim fallout included agitation, anxiety, depression, headaches, nausea, and sleep difficulties. And even after stalking has long ceased, victims often endure an eroded sense of well-being.

Mike Proctor is a retired California police detective and a stalking expert. "Many of the victims I have dealt with are at the end of their emotional tethers," he writes in his book *Antidote for a Stalker.* "Some have told me that they would rather be dead than try to survive another day...Some have made out wills. Others have armed themselves. Others have become prisoners in their own homes, terrified to go out into the world for fear of what the stalker will do next."

And with justification. For stalking victims can be physically injured or even killed by those who pursue them. In a study headed by London forensic psychiatrist David James, MD, all non-terrorist attacks on elected politicians in Western Europe between 1990 and 2004 were identified and evaluated for their impact on victims. There were 24 attacks; eight led to serious injuries, five more even to death. The fatalities included a government minister, a political party leader, and an aid to a member of parliament. In Dressing's stalking investigation, almost a third of victims had been physically assaulted by their pursuers, and almost a fifth had been sexually attacked.

So, which stalkers are the most lethal?

WHICH STALKERS ARE THE MOST DANGEROUS?

Perhaps you recall the movie *The Natural*, starring Robert Redford? It was based on the life of a baseball player named Eddie Waitkus, who played for the Chicago Cubs back during the 1940s. One day a woman named Ruth Ann Steinhagen saw Waitkus playand became enamored with him. She papered the walls of her room with photos of, and news clippings about, him. She even set a place for him at her dinner table.

In 1949, Waitkus was traded to a Philadelphia baseball team, which angered Steinhagen greatly. When she learned that Waitkus was to return with his new team to Chicago on June 14 of that year, she devised a plan for revenge.

She booked a room in the hotel where Waitkus was to stay—the Edgewater Hotel. On the evening of June 14, she moved into the room, downed a daiquiri and two whiskey sours, then paid a bellhop to deliver a note to Waitkus's room. The note read: "It is extremely important that I see you as soon as possible. We are not acquainted, but I have something of importance to speak to you about. I think it would be to your advantage to let me explain it to you."

Waitkus received the note and agreed to meet her. She shot him with a rifle, purportedly telling him that if she couldn't have him, nobody could.

Waitkus survived the shooting and returned to baseball, but never to his initial form.

This anecdote illustrates a finding from Mullen and his team: Female stalkers can be just as virulent as male stalkers. When 40 female stalkers were compared to 150 male ones, the former had been just as ready to attack as the latter. Such a finding may be somewhat surprising considering that men tend to be physically stronger and more aggressive than women are.

But perhaps even more unexpected, youngsters who stalk may be even more dangerous than men and women who do so. In the youth-stalking study conducted by Mullen and colleagues, over half the victims had been physically attacked, several suffered head injuries or lost consciousness after being strangled, and five were assaulted sexually. One was a 14-year-old girl who was raped by her former boyfriend on the school grounds.

Keep these findings in mind when planning any strategy to protect yourself or your youngsters from stalkers.

Still another thing you might want to consider in outfitting yourself or your youngsters against stalkers: Unless you are public figures, you are probably more likely to be stalked by someone you know than by a stranger

In the Dressing study, 76 percent of victims had been stalked by somebody they knew.

CAN YOU EXPECT A WARNING BEFORE AN ATTACK?

During the 1990s, two employees of the United States Secret Service, forensic psychologist Robert Fein, PhD, and senior agent Bryan Vossekuil, launched a research project that they hoped would help law enforcement officials identify would-be attackers of public figures before the individuals actually launched an attack.

First, they scanned historical databases to identify any individuals who had attempted, between 1949 and 1996, to attack or kill a public figure. The public figure could have been, for example, a president, a vice-president, a governor, a mayor, a visiting head of state, a corporate executive, or a celebrity. They located 83 such individuals. Then they attempted to learn something about them. And one of the things they found was that only 10 percent of the 83 had given their targets advance notice of their sinister intent.

In the study of the 24 stalkers who had attacked European politicians, headed by David James, MD, half had given an advanced warning. For the most part, the warnings were not threats, but rather indications of serious mental illness such as rambling thoughts or disjointed speech. Psychosis seems to be especially prevalent among politician attackers.

In a celebrity stalker study, California forensic psychiatrist Park

Dietz, MD, PhD, and colleagues found no link between threats and approach.

Moreover, in an evaluation of 86 individuals who had tracked members of Congress, Dietz and coworkers discovered that if the individuals had mailed their threats, they were *even less likely* to approach their targets than those who did not mail threats. On the other hand, while these results were statistically significant, one out of three of the stalkers who mailed threats *did* approach their targets.

And when individuals are hunted by a prior sexual intimate, they *do* usually receive a warning before the stalker attacks, J. Reid Meloy, PhD, and his colleagues point out.

So, all things considered, it looks as if stalkers may or may not give advanced notice of their plans to attack.

In any event, when they *do* issue threats, the threats that you should probably take the most seriously are those of a gruesome and chilling nature suggesting that the hunter is closing in on you and about to do you in. It could be a hearse that pulls up in front of your door, a bullet on your pillow, a dead bird in your mailbox. In a study of federal officials who had been targeted by stalkers, only one percent of the threats delivered via phone or mail and only three percent of the threats delivered verbally led a lethal outcome, whereas 41 percent of the threats delivered via baleful gestures or deeds did.

When stalkers harm their victims, where does it usually happen? Usually face to face, but not always. Shortly after 9/11, you may recall, that is, in the fall of 2001, letters containing virulent anthrax spores or powder were mailed to various people, including some lawmakers on Capitol Hill. The anthrax deliveries killed five individuals and injured 17 others. Finally in 2008, it looked as if the perpetrator had been identified. It was a biodefense scientist in Fort Dietrick, Maryland working on an anthrax vaccine. Yet before the investigators could file charges against him and arrest him, he apparently took his own life.

If you are being stalked, here are some measures you might consider taking to protect yourself. They come from retired police detective and stalking expert Mike Proctor.

Develop a security plan. For instance, if you use a global positioning system (GPS) device, do not enter your home address in it in case the stalker gets a hold of the device. Instead, enter an address close enough to your home that the device can get you back to the area.

If you have a neighborhood watch program, you might want to alert those running it to your stalker and ask them to give you a heads-up if he appears in your neighborhood.

If you are employed, let your boss or the human resources department know about your stalker so they can help you develop a safety plan.

Call your local police department and ask for the name and phone number of the officer who handles stalking cases or domestic violence cases. Then call that individual and solicit his help. If he doesn't provide it, go over his head to the detective lieutenant, and if that doesn't lead to anything, contact the detective commander. If that still doesn't bear any fruit, contact the department chief.

Keep a detailed record of all efforts your stalker makes to contact you. Save text messages from him. Place any notes, cards, gifts, or warnings from him in a plastic bag. A prosecutor may need such material to successfully prosecute your stalker.

Even if you feel some sympathy for your stalker, cut off all contact and carefully document not only the day, but even the time, that you did it. Such details may be necessary to successfully prosecute the person.

Walk, jog, or run against traffic, not with it. This way you can see whether your stalker is driving in your direction and escape before he has a chance to stop his car, hop out, and nab you.

Don't fall for the "broken wing" ruse. This is a technique that not just stalkers, but rapists and serial killers sometimes use to win a woman's sympathy and kill her. The villain wraps one of his arms with bandages or puts it in a sling, making it appear that he has broken his arm. He then approaches the woman he's interested in and asks whether she can help him put packages or other items in his car. If she says yes and gives him some assistance, he can grab her and push her into his car. Infamous serial killer Ted Bundy used this ploy with his victims.

Consider the pros and cons of getting a restraining order, that is, a legal order to protect you from your stalker. In some jurisdictions, if stalking occurs while the restraining order is in place, the stalker can be charged with a felony. But in Mike Proctor's opinion, if restraining orders are not backed by a strong law-enforcement presence, they aren't worth much.

Keep in mind that quick thinking upon encounter with your stalker might save your life. A number of years ago, a man obsessed with television anchorwoman Jessica Savitch managed to sneak past security guards and enter her office. She was startled. And scared. But instead of losing her cool, she acted as if she was happy to see him. While she carried on some banal conversation with him, she slowly eased her way toward her office door, stepped into the hall, shut the door quickly, locked it, then ran for help.

FOURTEEN

HOW TO PROTECT YOURSELF AND YOUR LOVED ONES FROM SEXUAL PREDATORS

Let me tell you a story based on something that really happened. I have changed the details to protect the identity of the people involved.

A man, whom we'll call Bob, was happily married and had a great sex life with his wife. But he craved sexual excitement from other sources as well.

For instance, he found that a brunette who lived on the next street over from his turned him on. *What a luscious chick!"* he told himself. *I've never seen such enticing boobs or butt!* So occasionally he would drive by her house on his way home from work. And if he saw her working in her garden, he would feel perspiration drip into his collar and would hear his own rapid breathing. After that, he would drive up the street a bit, park, zip open his pants, and gratify himself.

He would then proceed on home, pull up into his driveway, open his front door, and call to his wife: "Hi Honey! How was your day?"

Welcome to the byzantine world of sex predators, whose sexual behaviors may be relatively conventional or wildly imaginative; largely innocuous or even amusing; or deadly serious, with devastating psychological effects on the victim. The one factor uniting all of these behaviors is that the individuals targeted by them do not welcome them. *It is never a case of consensual sex.*

First, let's take a look at voyeurism—spying on an unsuspecting person to get a sexual high. This is perhaps the least egregious of the sexual predator behaviors since voyeurs do not touch their victims and since the targeted individuals are usually not aware of being violated.

Bob, described above, was a voyeur.

At first glance, one might wonder why voyeurs go to all the trouble of spying on women when they could simply get their sexual thrills by hanging out in strip clubs. The answer, it seems, has to do with consent. Strippers are willing to show off their bodies to strangers in order to earn money; voyeurs only want to ogle the bodies of women who *have not given them permission to do so.*

However, strippers *can* be a turn-on when they morph from strippers back into private citizens, one voyeur attested.

Sometimes "Peeping Toms" go to great lengths to get their sexual kicks, for example, by climbing a ladder or tree to peer through a window. Other Peeping Toms, however—perhaps the lazier or less enterprising ones—settle for sexual recharging right at home. One drilled a hole through his apartment wall so that he could spy on the woman living next door to him.

PENISES ON DISPLAY

Now enter exhibitionists, who expose their private parts in public to unsuspecting and non-receptive victims. Exhibitionism is somewhat more pernicious than voyeurism since the individuals who are targeted are aware of what is happening and since exposing is often an "in-your-face" encounter. I can speak from first-hand experience here.

A number of years ago, a girlfriend and I were traveling by train in Europe. A middle-aged, stocky man entered our train compartment and sat down directly opposite from me. A few minutes later, I noticed that he was grinning. I wondered why. I looked down and saw that he had unzipped his trousers and was wiggling and jiggling his penis in my direction, as if to say, "Hey, look at me!" Was I shocked? Sure. Indignant? You bet! But before I could react, he had tucked his "partner in crime" back into his pants and had vanished from our compartment.

Only later did I come to realize that I had received a more or less perfunctory penis performance. Some "flashers" are considerably more ingenious in their staging. One, I understand, mailed a dozen glossy prints of his "manhood" to a young woman he wanted to titillate.

Although men seem to be much more prone than women to dropping their pants to dazzle unsuspecting victims, some women have also been caught in the act.

Then there's frotteurism, that is, rubbing up against an unwilling individual to get a sexual frisson. Because it is more of a hands-on than a hands-off form of sex predation, it can be more disturbing to victims than exhibitionism or voyeurism. Most frotteurs, like most exhibitionists, are male. However, they tend to be younger—in their teens or early twenties.

Why do certain people engage in voyeurism, exhibitionism, or frotteurism? It's a mystery. Sex- behavior experts suspect that both genetic and environmental factors are involved. In any event, individuals who indulge in one of these quirky behaviors also often do so in the other two as well. The more the merrier, right?

How about more egregious sexual offenses such as rape and child molestation? Do voyeurs, exhibitionists, and frotteurs pursue them as well? In many cases no, but in some cases yes, one study suggests.

In this study, researchers followed 208 male exhibitionists over a 13-year period. The researchers found that while 159 (76 percent) of the subjects did not commit another sexual offense during this period, 49 (24 percent) did. And of the 49, 19 (nine percent of the entire sample) committed rape or child molestation.

RAPE: IT'S NOT REALLY ABOUT SEX

Even though rape is a sex predator behavior, as are voyeurism, exhibitionism, and frotteurism, it differs drastically from the latter in a number of ways.

First off, motive. Voyeurism, exhibitionism, and frotteurism are essentially about obtaining sexual gratification. Rape, in contrast, is something far more malignant. It "is a crime of violence," Robert I. Simon, MD, a forensic psychiatrist affiliated with Georgetown University, tells us in his book *Bad Men Do What Good Men Dream*. "Most rapists have the precise purpose of humiliating and harming the victim. The rapist finds sexual pleasure in the victim's pain and fear."

A case that Roy Hazelwood, a Federal Bureau of Investigation (FBI) sex- predator profiler, was called in on a few years ago underscores Simon's observation. The case concerned a man named James Mitchell DeBardeleben. Hazelwood and his colleagues learned that DeBardeleben was not only a counterfeiter, but a rapist. He had stowed thousands of pornographic photos of women, bloody female garments, and audiotapes recorded while he was tormenting his rape victims.

The impact of rape on victims can be psychologically devastating, research has shown. Some 80 percent of them experience posttraumatic stress disorder (PTSD)– that is, symptoms such as nightmares and flashbacks that can last months, even years. "We rape victims find ourselves living with guilt, shame, anger, outrage, fear, lack of trust, and even despair," one wrote.

What malevolent forces alchemize a young person into a rapist? Perhaps both genes and environment. But certainly environment.

There was once a young police officer in San Diego named Henry Hubbard, Jr. His fellow police officers thought that he was a regular guy; certainly while he was on duty, he was kind and caring towards women. Then they learned, to their astonishment, that he was also a vicious rapist who had attacked a number of women.

It turned out that Hubbard was a "Dr. Jekyll-Mr. Hyde" following in his father's footsteps. His father had been a respected teacher and school administrator. Yet on weekends, the father would descend into drunken rages and hit Henry and his mother, sometimes while brandishing a gun at them.

CHILD MOLESTATION: THE ULTIMATE SEX VIOLATION

If there is any group of people feared and loathed by society, it is undoubtedly child molesters.

With good reason. Sex molestation during childhood has been found capable of unleashing an unbelievable spectrum of psychiatric illnesses. Moreover, it can have an inter-generational effect: The offspring of people who were sexually abused as children are at a heightened risk of suicide even if they themselves have not experienced such maltreatment.

Thanks to media coverage in recent years, notably of the child sex abuse scandal in the Catholic Church, you can't help but get the impression that child molestation is a pervasive and pernicious problem. But is that really the case? Child-molestation experts are convinced that it is.

"Pedophilia is endemic in our society and affects not only the afflicted individual, but many, many others in the community as well," Fred Berlin, MD, a Johns Hopkins University associate professor of psychiatry and a leading authority on pedophilia, told me in an interview for *Psychiatric News.*

"We are seeing a huge increase in arrests for possession of child pornography over the Internet or for solicitation and enticement of children over the Internet," Richard Krueger, MD, medical director of New York State Psychiatric Institute's sexual behavior clinic, attested.

"If you had a child who had been molested, you would certainly say that it is a significant problem!" Howard Zonana, MD, declared. Zonana, a Yale University professor of psychiatry, chaired the American Psychiatric Association's Task Force on Sexual Offenders a few years ago.

Who are the people who prey upon our youngsters?

Many have pedophilic tendencies, that is, they sexually desire children. Nonetheless, their sexual desires for children may vary. Some prefer boys; others prefer girls; still others like both. Some molest children only inside their families; others molest children only outside; still others do both.

Some evidence, however sparse, suggests that genes might preen people to be pedophiles. A 1994 study found that 17 percent of pedophilic subjects had other pedophiles in their families, whereas only 3 percent of control subjects did. In 2011, Italian researchers reported that they had found an abnormal version of a particular gene in a man with pedophilia. This was a gene called the progranulin gene. When this gene was disrupted in rats, the rats engaged in abnormal sexual behavior. Then in 2013, a Finnish study of some 4,000 twins found that pedophilic interest was more prominent in identical twins than in fraternal twins, suggesting a genetic contribution to it.

There is substantial evidence that traumatic childhood experiences, notably sexual abuse, can set young people up to become pedophiles themselves. In his research over the years, Gene Abel, MD, medical director of the Behavioral Medicine Institute of Atlanta, Georgia, found that about 30 percent of pedophiles had been sexually abused as children. Research conducted by two pedophile experts at Beth Israel Medical Center in New York City—Igor Galynker, MD, PhD, and Lisa Cohen, PhD—has produced an even higher figure of 60 percent (versus only four percent in control subjects).

Brain aberrations may also contribute to pedophilia, Galynker and Cohen have found. They showed a film of an adult molesting a girl to both a group of male pedophiles who had molested girls and to a group of control subjects. The film was found to sexually arouse the pedophiles more than the controls. (The size of penile erection was used to measure the degree of subjects' sexual arousal.) Furthermore, the researchers used brain imaging to track the brain activity of the pedophiles and of the controls while watching the film. The researchers compared results from the two groups.

The pedophiles experienced more activity in the frontal lobes and temporal lobes of the brain during this period than the controls did. The human brain has two frontal lobes—one on the left and one on the right in the front part of the brain. It also has two temporal lobes—one located on the left side of the brain behind the left frontal lobe and one located on the right side of the brain behind the right frontal lobe. The frontal lobes are known to be implicated in impulse control, the temporal lobes in sexual response.

Pedophilic interest or activity has likewise been linked with the release of abnormally high levels of sex hormones by the pituitary—a pea-sized gland located at the base of the brain—a small study conducted by pedophilia expert Fred Berlin, MD, and his colleagues implied.

Just as opiate drugs can produce a psychological high, so can opiate compounds naturally present in the brain. Brain imaging research conducted by Berlin and his group in normal (non-pedo-philic) subjects suggested that one of the things that occurs in the brain during sexual arousal is the release of endogenous opiates. "That may explain why, for some people, sex seems so addicting," Berlin ventured. And a spurt in such opiates during sexual arousal might also contribute to pedophilia in some way, he speculated.

Nonetheless, what may come as a surprise to many of us is that "there is no difference in sex drive between a person with pedophilia and a person with normal sexual interest," a sexual behavior expert told me. "I've seen people with very high sex drives who have a per-fectly normal sexual interest, and I have also seen pedophiles with extremely low sex drives," she said.

Also perplexing, even to pedophile experts, is why so many pedophiles have schizotypal personality disorder, that is, a way of distorting reality. This finding "is interesting," Cohen remarked, "because one of the things that pedophiles are known for is cognitive distortions where they rationalize, minimalize, or distort what they are doing." For instance, they might say, 'I'm not abusing children; they need to know about sex.' Or they might say, 'I didn't molest her; she seduced me!'"

But it can get even worse: child sex molesters who are also rap-ists. They molest children not because they are sexually attracted to them, but because they want to hurt them.

One such appalling individual was admitted to Galynker's clinic following a child pornography bust. The pornography that this person had enjoyed was so obscene that it made his defense lawyer literally sick to her stomach, Galynker told me.

Yet even more nauseating are the acts actually carried out by such vile individuals. In May 2005, a man named Joseph E. Duncan III entered the house of the Groene family in Coeur d'Alene, Idaho.

He brutally murdered the mother, her fiancé, and her older son. He then kidnapped the nine-year-old daughter Shasta and the younger son Dylan and drove them into the Montana wilderness, where, over a period of weeks, he repeatedly tortured and raped them. He then killed Dylan, drove back into Coeur d'Alene with Shasta, and took her with him into a Denny's Restaurant to eat breakfast. The manager of Denny's, a waitress at Denny's, and two Denny's customers recognized Shasta from a missing person's photo and surreptitiously called the police. Duncan was arrested and confessed to the odious things he had done.

How did Duncan become such a monster? A traumatic childhood environment was probably one reason, testimony given at his competency hearing by his sister, Cheri Duncan Cox, suggests.

When she and Duncan were children, Cox reported, their mother regularly beat them while ranting that men were worthless. The derision was essentially directed toward her husband and the children's father, a military man who was often deployed elsewhere. Moreover, Duncan reacted passively to these beatings and rantings, Cox noted. He didn't show anger, and he didn't fight back. It is thus plausible that Duncan internalized any rage and hate he felt towards his mother while she was abusing him, yet eventually vented such vitriolic emotions by brutalizing other children. Indeed, at age 15, he raped a boy at gun point. By age 16, he had raped another 12.

Did Duncan inherit any "mean genes," or did he incur any brain damage that might have propelled him into a career of rape and torture? The answer isn't known, but it's possible. For as we saw in Chapter 6, some individuals who have committed heinous crimes, including child molestation, have been found to possess abnormally small prefrontal cortexes. The prefrontal cortex is the foremost part of the frontal lobe. And since each of us has two frontal lobes, each of us also has two prefrontal cortexes. Your prefrontal cortexes are located behind your eyes. They are known to be crucial for moral judgment.

All things considered, child molesters seem to fall into essentially two groups: One is motivated by sexual desire, the other by vile emotions such as hate and vengeance. Both groups may have been prepped for their nefarious careers by specific genes; devastating childhood experiences, notably sexual abuse; or by brain abnormalities. But at the end of the day, there is still this question: Even if certain individuals are prone to child molestation because of certain genes, environmental insults, or brain defects, what prompts them to take the leap and actually molest a child? Could it be free will? Unfortunately, forensic science can't say.

ARMING YOURSELF AGAINST SEX PREDATORS

So here they are, a wide swath of sex predators. How do you protect yourself and your loved ones from them, especially those of a more despicable nature?

Voyeurs. The best way to shield yourself from voyeurs is pretty much an open-and-shut case – literally. Close your blinds and curtains once it starts to get dark. This simple measure should keep anyone interested in ogling you and your loved ones from doing so. Moreover, any Peeping Tom who has even more heinous intentions, such as raping you or molesting your children, will be less likely to carry out the act if he isn't familiar with your daily habits.

Exhibitionists. What time of year are you most likely to encounter an exhibitionist? Yes, you're right, in the warmer months. Exhibitionists don't want to get frostbite on their private parts. Now, where is the public place where you would probably be least likely to encounter an exhibitionist? I bet you won't guess this one: It's a nudist resort!

There are two reasons why, a sexual-behavior expert told me. Exhibitionists find being around naked strangers incredibly intoxicating, yet most nudist resorts frown on overt sexual arousal. Exhibitionists only want to show off their private parts to individuals who don't want to see them. People who frequent nudist resorts obviously do.

But let's be realistic: Who wants to stay home during the warmer months or hang out on nude beaches just to avoid exhibitionists? A better tactic would probably be to keep in mind that exhibitionists are known to be creatures of habit, often frequenting the same locations and targeting the same types of victims. Thus, if you happen to cross paths with one, you could avoid his hunting ground in the future, or better yet, alert the police to the person's whereabouts so they could make an arrest.

Frotteurs. Crowded subway trains and busses, not surprisingly, are undoubtedly frotteurs' favorite haunts because they can easily sidle up to a potential victim and rub against her or him to get their sexual charge. And if they are lucky, their victims won't even be aware of such abuse. So the best way to protect yourself against frotteurs in crowded public transportation is to stay on the alert, and if you feel someone rubbing against you, get off at the next stop and report the incident to the subway station manager or a comparable person with the transportation authority. If it's a subway situation, the manager can radio the train conductor, who can then arrange for a police inspector to board the subway before the frotteur gets off and, possibly, even make an arrest.

Law enforcement officials used to take a cavalier attitude toward frotteurs. That is fortunately no longer the case, a sexual behavior authority attests. Public service ads are also being placed in subway cars to raise awareness of frotteurs among the public and to tell them what to do if they are accosted by one.

Sometimes frotteurs lurk in subway tunnels. Many years ago, when I was a college student, I took the subway to classes early in the morning when there were few, if any, other people in the subway system. One morning, a man tackled me from behind as I was walking through the subway tunnel, threw me to the ground, and ran his hand up under my skirt. Before I could come to my senses and yell at him, he had gotten his titillation and darted away.

SoOne way to avoid being accosted by a frotteur in a subway tunnel, I suggest, is to occasionally glance behind you as you make your way through the tunnel. Yet if, in spite of this precaution, you are still assaulted, report it immediately to the subway station manager. Hopefully your quick action will lead to the perpetrator's arrest and keep him from launching any more subway tunnel attacks on you or other victims.

Rapists. It is a dark and desolate night. The footsteps are getting closer. I hurry to unlock my apartment building door. Yet just as I am about to slip into the foyer, a powerful hand grabs me around the neck, yanks me back onto the sidewalk, and drags me around the corner of the building into the alley. I can smell his fetid breath; I can hear his animal grunts. I now know that there's no escape, I know what's coming.

Whenever women think about the dangers of being raped, they often envision such terrifying scenarios. The rapist, a stranger, attacks in the gloom. He is surly, monstrous, grotesque. Indeed, some rapists do fit this profile. But what many women—perhaps most women—don't realize is this shocking fact: Women are more likely to be raped by somebody they know than by a stranger.

If you doubt that this is the case, consider the results of one national study of female rape victims. It found that 59 percent had been raped by someone they knew—20 percent by a friend; 16 percent by a husband; 14 percent by a boyfriend; and nine percent by a neighbor, coworker, handyman, or some other acquaintance. Still another study found that one out of eight college women are raped, again, often by somebody they know. I have a friend who had such an experience, and it happened even though she was attending one of the country's most prestigious universities.

Still more troubling, forensic psychiatrist Robert Simon, MD, points out, is that there are no easy ways to determine which of the men you know might be a closet rapist. Many hold down good jobs, many are married, many have children. And those men who rape on a regular basis tend to be highly intelligent, highly articulate, interesting, even fun to be around—until they attack.

It looks as though any woman concerned about rape needs two different strategies to protect herself: one to deal with strangers who might be rapists and one to deal with men she knows who might be. First, some ploys that might protect you from stranger rapists.

One researcher had the ingenuous idea of interviewing imprisoned rapists to learn something about their habits before being caught and which factors had made them more or less likely to target a specific woman. He found that supermarket parking lots, office parking garages, and public restrooms had been their favorite hunting grounds for victims; that they had been more likely to attack a woman with long hair than a woman with short hair because long hair—whether worn hanging, in a ponytail, or in a braid—would give them something to grab onto; and that they had been reluctant to attack women carrying umbrellas because the women could have used the umbrellas as weapons against them.

The take-home message from these findings is this: Beware of rapists in supermarket parking lots, office parking garages, and public restrooms, particularly when no one else is around. Carry something that can be used as a weapon. And if you have long hair, consider tucking it in a hat or cutting it.

Make sure that your home is impregnable to rapists lurking without. Recently, a woman living in the prestigious Kalorama neighborhood of Washington, DC (where former President Barack Obama and billionaire Jeff Bezos live) was raped in her home. "I don't know how the rapist got in!" she confessed to her neighbors and friends.

Now, let's consider several ploys that might protect you from men you know who are secret rapists. They come from Joan Meijer, a date- rape victim back in college and author of *Date Rape: It's Not Your Fault.*

A number of years ago, Meijer visited her grandparents during college spring break. Since they lived near a beach, she spent a good part of her visit hanging out there, swimming and chatting with the lifeguards. After a few days, one, whom we'll call Tad, asked her out for a cup of coffee. She breezily accepted. They drove to a coffee shop together, ordered coffee, and had a chat. Tad said that he would drive her home. As they neared her grandparents' house, however, he pulled off onto a golf course, parked, and started kissing and fondling her.

"It was nice," Meijer recalls. "I didn't think much about it. Parking was the norm in those days. My dates and I would neck, we'd fool around, but they always stopped when I said, 'That's enough!'" Tad's fondling and kissing, though, quickly escalated into an effort to undress her, and when she protested and fought back, he pinned her under the steering wheel and raped her.

Later, Meijer pondered how she might have avoided this fiasco. She recalled that two other lifeguards had been present when Tad asked her out, and that they had exchanged a look—a look that had made her wonder, *What do they know and I don't?* Yet she had ignored this warning sign that something wasn't quite right and gone ahead and placed herself in harm's way. So, if you ever feel that something isn't quite right about a man or a situation, don't ignore it, she advises. It might safeguard you from rape.

But Meijer goes even further with her advice: "Don't allow yourself to be alone with any male (friend, family member, family friend, or date) if you don't know them well enough to trust them. Even if you think you can trust them, think twice. Never assume you can trust anyone. These statements are not about all men being bad. These statements are about being proactively protective of yourself...being personally responsible for your own safety."

Child Molesters. On May 25, 1979, a six-year-old boy named Etan Patz vanished while walking from his apartment in New York City's Soho District to his school bus stop two blocks away. It was the first time that his parents had let him walk to the bus stop alone. Only 38 years later—in 2017—was his abductor identified and convicted. It was a man named Pedro Hernandez. Hernandez had worked in a convenience store near Etan's bus stop and had used the promise of a soda to lure him into the store's basement. After that, Hernandez sexually molested and killed the boy.

On October 1, 1993, in the quiet town of Petaluma in Northern California, a 12-year-old girl named Polly Klaas was kidnapped while hosting a slumber party in her bedroom. The perpetrator turned out to be Richard Allen Davis, a seasoned criminal who, in a drug rush, had randomly sought Polly out to abduct, sexually abuse, and murder.

When parents read about such appalling cases, they dread that something equally devastating could befall their own youngsters, and they ask themselves: *What can I do to protect them?*

The answer, as it turns out, is a "lot."

First off, it's critical to clear up some common misconceptions about child molesters. Yes, strangers do sometimes kidnap, sexually molest, and kill children. But children are sexually abused more often by someone they know than by a stranger, Robin Sax, a Los Angeles deputy district attorney who has prosecuted numerous child molesters, tells us. "I often remind parents that if they want to worry, they should worry about the people they know as well as about the ones they don't," she writes in her book *Predators and Child Molesters: What Every Parent Needs to Know to Keep Kids Safe.*

And if that isn't disconcerting enough, the villains are often people who hold positions of authority over children. Athletic coaches, camp counselors, day care workers, elementary school teachers, and even physicians have been convicted of child sexual abuse. So have numerous Catholic priests and also some Protestant ministers, Jewish rabbis, and Native American healers.

"These unpleasant facts are not intended to attack the integrity of [such professionals]," Sax stresses. "The truth is, most…are highly professional, honest, and upright…[But] to say that sexual assault doesn't occur in schools, churches, temples, and so on is as unrealistic as saying that police officers, lawyers, and judges never lie!"

Moreover, while men perpetrate the lion's share of child sexual abuse, women are sometimes the perpetrators as well, Fabian Saleh, MD, director of the sexual disorders clinic at the University of Massachusetts, told me during an interview for *Psychiatric News.* "We are conducting a study on female sex offenders and their psychological makeup to see whether they differ from male sex offenders," he said.

And child sex-offender expert Gene Abel, MD, shares an even more startling and disturbing discovery with us: Although most people would probably guess that the average age of child molesters is 25 or 30 years, in fact it is only 13 years! The reason why may be because many child molesters were themselves abused as children. It's thus conceivable that only several years after being abused, they launch their own abuse careers.

Armed with the above knowledge, you're now in a position to map out a strategy to protect your youngsters from child molesters.

Following are some tactics that you might consider incorporating into your plan.

Know the tools that laws give you to protect your children. On July 29, 1994—only 10 months after Polly Klaas's abduction, sexual abuse, and murder—another child endured a similarly horrific fate in Hamilton Township, New Jersey. Seven-year-old Megan Kanka was lured by a neighbor into his house; he then raped and strangled her. He was a convicted sex offender, but Megan's parents didn't know that.

National outrage over this tragedy led to the passage of a federal law known informally as "Megan's Law." Once convicted child sex offenders are released from prison, they are supposed to keep law enforcement agencies informed on where they are residing. This way, agencies can track their whereabouts, and parents can learn whether any convicted child molesters live in their area.

Thanks to the internet, parents can now obtain such information online—either through state or national Web sites. For instance, if you visit the free national Web site for Family Watchdog, all you have to do is type in your address. A map will appear showing you whether any child molesters live near you and where. You can click on the molesters listed to learn more about them: their names, their addresses, what they look like, and their previous offenses.

Checking online to see whether any convicted child molesters live near you is a powerful tool for protecting your children from them, Sax attests. She cautions, however, that it is far from foolproof because the system depends on the honesty of convicted molesters and many fail to register where they are currently living.

The old advice, "Don't talk to strangers," still has currency for protecting youngsters from sex offenders. But it needs to be expanded to "Don't talk to strangers on the Internet," Sax emphasizes. Children should be warned that people online are not always who they say they are—that they might be child molesters—and that they should never respond to an e-mail, text, or instant message if they don't know who sent it.

Locking your doors is one way to keep strangers from sneaking into your house and molesting your children. This is easier said than done, I know, with youngsters and their friends coming and going to and from the house all day long. But it should be easier once dinner time comes and once it starts to get dark outside.

Ironically, in October 2003, a decade to the month after Polly Klaas was kidnapped from her home in Petaluma, California, then sexually assaulted and murdered, residents of Petaluma were once again leaving their houses unlocked at night. And once again, a sex predator was making the rounds. On one occasion, the predator slipped into an unlocked house at 4:30 a.m. and attempted to remove the pants of a sleeping girl. Fortunately, she had the presence of mind to tell him that she had to go to the bathroom, then raced to her parents' bedroom to let them know what was happening. Her father chased the predator out of the house and down the street, but unfortunately lost him.

Impress upon your children that while most adults and teens are okay folks, there are some bad apples out there, and it may even be someone they know such as a teacher, a scout leader, a sports coach, a babysitter, a camp counselor, or even a relative. In other words, tell them that molesters don't always look creepy and may appear to be warm, caring, and respectful.

Moreover, you might point out to your youngsters that predators sometimes use clever ploys to cozy up to targeted victims. For instance, a neighbor who is a predator might ask a child to do some yard work for him. A sports coach who is a predator might offer a child a ride home. Also, keep in mind that some predators try to butter parents up in order to get access to their youngsters. A friend of mine had this happen. A teacher said to her: "Your little boy is so interesting, so delightful! Could he visit me at home?" Fortunately, my friend saw through the ruse and said, "No."

Impress upon your children, as Sax stresses, that their body is their own, and that no one should be able to touch it without their permission. In fact, if somebody tries to do so *even* with a child's permission, it might be a red flag that they're up to no good. When I was an adolescent, a man in my family (I won't name names!) asked me to sit on his lap. I reluctantly did so. "What a gorgeous young chick you're becoming!" His voice was thick with possibilities. I found his behavior unsettling and suspicious. I still do.

Perhaps the most crucial thing you can do to safeguard your children from sex offenders is to tell them to avoid being alone with any adult or teen they don't know well. If this sounds like extreme advice, well, okay, it is, but it is buttressed by the following true story.

For some years now, a man has been marching back and forth in front of the Vatican embassy in Washington, DC, holding a sign that says "The Vatican Hides Pedophiles." One day I decided to walk up Massachusetts Avenue, NW, to where the embassy is located. I wanted to talk with him and learn why he was doing all this protesting.

His name was John Wojnowski. When he was a youngster, he told me, a Catholic priest he knew lured him into the priest house on some pretense, then sexually abused him. The experience devastated him psychologically. He was too ashamed to tell his parents what had happened and became withdrawn and depressed. Although the experience did not change his sexual orientation, it nonetheless contributed to the failure of his eventual marriage. He's even convinced that the psychological trauma resulting from the assault stunted his growth because he ended up being much shorter than other men in his family.

"So," I said, "I think I now understand why you've been protesting all these years. You want the world to know that some Catholic priests are depraved and dangerous, and that the Vatican has been protecting them rather than reporting them to the police. Is that correct?"

"Yes, that's right," he replied.

"But I do have a question about your particular experience. Suppose you hadn't fallen for the priest's ruse and hadn't entered his house. Then you would have never been abused in the first place, correct?"

"Yes, maybe," he admitted.

FIFTEEN
HOW TO KEEP FROM BECOMING AN EVILDOER OR TURNING YOUR CHILDREN INTO ONE

No, you are not Dr. Hannibal Lecter from the 1991 movie thriller *The Silence of the Lambs*. And, no, you do not eat your patients' livers! But let's face it: You, I, all of us must have a weakness for the Dark Side. Otherwise, how could we be fascinated by such a film?

The same goes for the Netflix series *A House of Cards*, which debuted in 2013 and which even President Obama enjoyed, I understand. If we weren't attracted to the Dark Side, how could we be smitten by appalling Congressman Frank Underwood and his delicious, but equally malicious, wife Claire?

Yet, you're only enjoying baseness vicariously when you watch such films, right? In real life, you would never do such things! But don't be so sure.

Michael Nelken, MD, a University of Connecticut psychoanalyst, once ventured: "Impulses to do evil fly thick and fast all day long. Evil is always present, in every mind."

Robert Simon, MD, a clinical professor of psychiatry at

Georgetown University, has written: "The sadistic traits seen in such serial killers as Jeffrey Dahmer have their tamer counterparts in patients who will never commit a sexually sadistic crime of any kind, who are respectable persons, good mothers and fathers, successful professionals. I have treated solid citizens who mentally torture their spouses, children, elderly parents, and themselves, but would not dream of raising a finger to physically harm anyone."

And as psychiatrist Lloyd Sederer, MD, posted March 4, 2014 in *The Huffington Post:* "While virtue may evoke admiration, evil excites…Evil has a perverse beauty to it. It always has. Satan was an angel before his fall. Whether you see evil in a religious context, demonic in nature, or in a secular manner, as wrongful behavior driven by self-absorption, it requires its opposite, namely good, to give it shape and meaning. What's more, the greater the tension between good and evil, the more we can appreciate its presence and its force."

If you are still not convinced that there are evil impulses in all of us, then let's take a look at what a famous, or rather infamous, psychology experiment has to tell us.

The year was 1961. Yale University psychology professor Stanley Milgram, PhD launched an experiment to find out how far ordinary folks would go in inflicting pain on another human being simply because an authoritarian figure pressured them into doing so.

He placed an advertisement in a newspaper in New Haven, Connecticut where Yale is located looking for men who were willing to participate in what he billed as a learning and memory experiment at Yale. Out of the men who applied, he selected 40 to be his subjects. They ranged in age from 20 to 50 years and held down jobs from unskilled to professional.

At the start of the experiment, each subject was told he was a teacher and that he was being matched with a "student," who was actually not a student, but in cahoots with Milgram. He was also introduced to a "scientist," who was really not a scientist, but in cahoots with Milgram as well.

The subject (teacher) and phony scientist were put in one room, which contained an electric- shock generator and a row of switches marked from 15 volts (slight shock) up to 450 volts (severe shock). The phony student was put in another room, strapped to a chair, and had electrodes attached to his arms. The subject (teacher) was then told by the phony scientist to administer test questions to the phony student, and every time the phony student did not answer correctly, to shock him, and at increasingly greater intensities.

If the subject (teacher) was reluctant to do so, the phony scientist would pressure him with comments such as "Please continue," or "It is absolutely essential that you continue," or "You have no choice but to continue." Meanwhile, the phony student in the other room was screaming from fake pain as the subject (teacher) followed the instructions of the phony scientist.

All 40 subjects (teachers) delivered up to 300 volts of electricity; two-thirds delivered shocks at the highest level of 450 volts.

Milgram's conclusions? Ordinary people are likely to follow orders given by an authoritarian figure, even to the extent of killing an innocent human being.

Well, you might rightfully protest, this experiment included only 40 subjects. How about the rest of us? Milgram went on to obtain similar results with other populations in similar experiments. And so did other researchers. As Philip Zimbardo, PhD, a professor of psychology at Stanford University, has written: Milgram's research results are "the most generalizable in all of social science, since they include dozens of systematic replications with 1,000 subjects from as diverse backgrounds as possible within the United States." They have also been replicated by investigators in Europe, Zimbardo noted.

And Zimbardo's ultimate conclusion? "Almost any of us, at least the majority of us, could change places with Eichmann if we fell under the power of the same situational forces as he faced." Adolf Eichmann, one of Hitler's henchmen, was responsible for the deaths of millions of Jews during the Nazis' reign of power in Germany, from 1933 to 1945.

The son of another top Hitler man, Hans Frank, appears to concur.

In 1939, Hans Frank was appointed governor general of occupied Poland by Hitler. His son Niklas was seven years old at the time and was raised in a castle. His mother would take him into town in a chauffeured limousine. There she would buy mink coats that belonged to Jewish women about to be sent to their deaths in the concentration camp Auschwitz. Despite these experiences, Niklas later wrote a book condemning what his father had done. It was published in 1991.

Evildoer expert Michael Stone, MD, wrote Niklas a letter, asking him whether he had any clue about why he had chosen the moral high ground. Niklas wrote back, saying that he had no answer. But Niklas did stress that he believed that the dangers of evildoing are present in all of us and asked: "Who knows whether, if I had been born in my father's time, I wouldn't have ended up like my father?"

I certainly agree from what a German friend, Ingrid, confided in me that the times people live in do influence whether the evil impulses percolating in them find expression or not.

Ingrid hardly remembers her father Fritz since she was only three years old when he set off to serve Hitler during World War II. Fritz was eventually sent to the Russian front, where he was killed by the Russians.

But as Ingrid later learned from her family, Fritz had been a passionate Nazi who had rejoiced at *Kristallnacht*. This was the night of November 9 to 10, 1938 where the Nazis torched synagogues; vandalized Jewish homes, schools, and businesses; and slaughtered close to 100 Jews.

Ingrid can also remember clearly how her brother Karl, her senior, got swept up in the Nazi fervor and joined the Hitler Youth Movement in 1942. The movement had been founded in 1926. By 1930, it had enlisted over 25,000 boys. Although it offered benign activities such as hiking and camping, it also indoctrinated youth in Nazi ideology after Hitler came to power. At one point, Karl envisioned that after Hitler took over Europe, he, Karl, would be named Mayor of London. Karl's dream did not come to pass; Hitler lost power on May 8, 1945 when Germany surrendered to the Allies.

These many decades later, times have changed dramatically for Germany. Germany is a democracy, and the Germans are still hard at work trying to make reparations for the atrocities committed under the Nazi regime. For instance, when hundreds of thousands of refugees made their way into Europe in 2015, German Chancellor Angela Merkel decided to engage in an open-door policy toward them. Over a million of the refugees were settled in Germany during 2015 and 2016.

And what is the position of Ingrid's brother Karl today as far as the Nazi years are concerned? "Hitler's dynasty was supposed to last 1,000 years," he told her recently. "But it only lasted 12!" She could hear the scorn in his voice. Yet suppose that Hitler's dynasty were still alive and well. Would he be expressing another view? "I don't know." Ingrid sighed. "I hope not. But I honestly don't know."

Thus, if you concede that you might, possibly might, be tempted to do something reprehensible, at least if the time, place, and circumstances pressured you into it, how could you keep from doing so?

EVILDOERS OFTEN START SMALL

Wanton individuals are rarely, if ever, born that way. They start off small, then work their way up. Various studies have documented this transition.

For example, a longitudinal study launched in New Zealand in 1972, and published in 1996, followed almost a thousand boys from childhood into adulthood. It found that even as early as three years of age, those boys who were impulsive, restless, and distracted were at risk of becoming antisocial young men. It also found that of those boys who, as young adults, ended up being antisocial, 60 percent had had a full-blown conduct disorder before age 15.

In his study of 130 serial killers, evildoer expert Michael Stone, MD, found that about a fifth had engaged during youth in bed wetting, fire setting, and animal torture. Many more had set fires and tortured animals. David Berkowitz, known for his lover's lane murders in 1976, had recorded the number of fires he set during his teen years—1,411. He had also tortured animals.

Moreover, "The boundary between good and evil can be shifted by any of us," psychoanalyst Michael Nelken, MD, asserts. "We can talk ourselves into things."

Repetition can also make it easier to do bad things. As serial killer Ian Brady once wrote, "Once the killer has committed the first or second act of homicide, he will gradually accept his own acts as normal or supra-normal, and that of the rest of humanity as subnormal and weak."

And doing bad things seems to feed the desire to do things that are even worse. As evildoer expert Michael Welner, MD, has noted: "I don't think [serial killer] Ted Bundy went out intentionally to kill

30 women. But he had an itch and would scratch it, and then he had the itch again. At some point the urge could not be kept at bay."

All the above grim news will hopefully help keep you, me, all of us from engaging in wanton behavior. But some good news will hopefully help us even more to take the high road.

Remember Oskar Schindler, the German *bon vivant* made famous in the Hollywood film "Schindler's List"? He was given control of a Jewish-owned factory in Poland after the Nazis took over Poland in 1939. At first he was only interested in getting rich from the factory. But then he started engaging in small acts of kindness to benefit his Jewish workers. After that, he took greater and greater risks to keep them alive and to spare them from the Nazis. Finally, he spent all of his wealth to do so. He ultimately saved 1,300 lives.

In brief: Just as small steps into evil can lead to bigger ones, small steps into good can do the same.

WATCH OUT FOR THE COMPANY YOU KEEP

As any crime buff knows, Bonnie and Clyde were infamous American criminals back during the 1930s, operating as a husband-and-wife team although they weren't married.

During the 1960s, England was cursed with an even more nefarious couple—child serial killer Ian Brady and his partner-in-crime Myra Hindley. Brady and Hindley first met during the early 1960s while working at a chemical factory. She became infatuated with the pseudo-intellectual Brady, who read Nazi documents in their original German while eating in the factory cafeteria. The pair soon discovered that they both enjoyed sadomasochistic sex and bondage, and, eventually, the torture and killing of children.

Could antisocial behavior be contagious? Maybe, a Canadian study suggests. The researchers randomly chose over 500 couples from a large, previously conducted general population survey; determined how many had engaged in antisocial behavior; then looked to see whether those individuals who had engaged in such behavior also had spouses who had done so. About 20 percent had, they learned. So be vigilant about people you or your children hang out with, or even more, want to marry!

Other types of bad company such as toxic music, violent computer games, or pornography can also place all of us on the slippery slope morally.

In 1999, Colorado teens Dylan Klebold and Eric Harris played brutal computer games and listened to decadent music before gunning down students at Columbine High School in Colorado. In 2002, Robert Steinhaeuser, a teen in Erfurt, Germany, indulged in similar passions before fatally shooting 13 teachers, two students, a policeman, and the temporary director of the high school.

Ample research documents the vitriolic influence of pornography, Gail Dines, PhD, a sociology professor at Wheelock College in Boston, tells us. In a study of American college men, for example, 83 percent reported watching mainstream pornography, and those who did were more likely to report that they would commit rape or sexual assaults if they could get away with it than were those who didn't watch mainstream pornography. In a content analysis of best-selling and most-rented porn films, researchers found that 88 percent contained physically aggressive content, such as choking, gagging, slapping, or spanking, and that 49 percent of them contained verbal abuse – say, calling a victim "bitch" or "slut." And, you guessed it: Almost all of the films were targeted against women, and 70 percent of the aggressors in the films were men.

But perhaps the strongest argument for keeping a safe distance from pornography comes from one of the most rapacious serial killers of the 20th Century—Ted Bundy. After he was arrested, tried, convicted, and imprisoned, Bundy admitted that he had been an afficionado of porn coupling sex with violence, and that the porn had helped him justify his crimes.

ANGER: AN UNEXPECTED ANTIDOTE

Not surprisingly, anger is a catalyst for many deplorable acts. Remember professional heavyweight boxer Mike Tyson? At the height of his career in the late 1980s and throughout the 1990's, he was one of the most recognized sports personalities in the world. Yet on June 28, 1997, he bit the right ear of his opponent Evander Holyfield in a moment of rage. The bite was severe enough to remove a piece of the ear. It was found on the ring floor after the fight.

So, should you try to suppress anger? No, Philadelphia psychoanalyst Henri Parens, MD, surprisingly advises us. The reason why, he explains, is because anger reflects emotional pain and may be justified. But what you *should* do, he stresses, is be careful about what you do with that anger.

Say, you're incensed at your boss because she put you down in front of your colleagues. Instead of confronting him about it—after all, you don't want to risk losing your job—you might consider using competitive sports to air and dampen your ire. For years, Parens used martial arts to vent his indignation.

Or say that a driver engages in road rage against you. Try to keep your cool and guess why he is so angry. Maybe he just learned that his father has cancer, or that his wife wants to divorce him. In any event, responding to anger with anger would only up the ante and perhaps escalate into tragic consequences for both of you.

And if there is any truly effective way to diffuse your wrath when somebody wrongs you, it is by trying to be understanding and forgiving, Parens argues. "In psychoanalysis, we never talk about goodness. We have ignored it. But it is a reservoir in all of us that is not tapped enough."

YET DON'T BE A PUSHOVER!

But too much altruism, that is, unreservedly putting another's needs before your own, sometimes leads to dire consequences. Consider the following true story.

In 1969, life was brimming with promise as a young couple took their marriage vows in the New York City suburb of Eastchester. They were Betty Bisceglia and Dan Broderick III.

Dan was in medical school at Cornell University. Betty looked forward to having a professionally successful husband and being a stay-at-home mom, a common practice in those years.

Betty got pregnant with their first child, daughter Kim, on their honeymoon. Four more children followed. After Dan graduated from medical school, he attended Harvard Law School, and during those years, Betty supported the family financially. Subsequently, Dan was offered employment at a law firm in San Diego, California. He accepted the offer, moved his family to San Diego, and started to specialize in medical-malpractice cases At this point, he was positioned to earn good money, and Betty was positioned to fulfill her dream: having a professionally successful husband and being a stay-at-home mom. A happy ending, no?

No. In 1983, Dan hired an attractive young woman, Linda Kolkena, as his legal assistant. Betty suspected Dan of having an affair with Linda and accused him of it. At first, he denied it, but later admitted that it was true. His marriage to Betty unraveled. He moved out of their house in 1985 and filed for divorce.

Their four-year-long bitter divorce proceedings garnered national attention, largely because the proceedings concerned legal issues involving women who had put their husbands through graduate or professional school. In 1989, Dan finally obtained a divorce, then married Linda Kolkena. Seven months later, Betty stole into Dan and Linda's house and shot them both to death.

Betty's revenge against Dan for using, then dumping her wasn't entirely sweet, though. She was tried and convicted of the killings and is today serving her sentence at the California Institution for Women in Chino, California.

Although women have traditionally been more likely than men to support their spouses financially and to later regret it with tragic consequences, some men have followed similar trajectories. Evildoer expert Michael Stone, MD, tells us about one such man.

He was an electrician who put his wife through law school. Yet while she was studying there, she met a fellow law student who turned her on and started having an affair with him. She sued her husband for divorce, moved out of their house, and sought custody of their daughter. When she returned to the house one morning to collect some belongings, her husband flew into a rage and shot her in the buttocks.

The shot wasn't fatal. But he had made his point.

MOUNT PLEASANT WASN'T SO PLEASANT

What with high-profile assassinations, civil-rights and feminist upheavals, America of the 1960's was pretty turbulent. Consequently, the year 1967 wasn't a particularly auspicious time to be born. That was certainly the case for a boy named Larry Swartz.

Larry was the offspring of a waitress and a pimp. His mother abandoned him at age 20 months in a Silver Spring, Maryland apartment. During the next six years, he was passed from one foster family to another. One foster mother broke his arm after he wet his bed.

In 1973, life finally seemed to be looking up for Larry. He was adopted by a couple who had wanted children, but who hadn't managed to have any. They were Bob and Kay Swartz. They lived on Mount Pleasant Drive in Annapolis, Maryland. But here, too, things didn't go well. The Swartzes had difficulty showing emotional warmth. They had high academic expectations that Larry failed to meet. For instance, Larry's school performance was mediocre, which upset Kay, and Larry had no interest in computers, which were Bob's passion. Bob and Kay were also strict disciplinarians. Larry was not allowed to date until he was age 16, and then he was not allowed to get a driver's license. Kay also made sure that he did not date any girl more than once.

It was snowing the night of January 16, 1984. Larry had finished his homework, and Kay was watching television. Kay asked Larry how he had done on his exams that day. "Good on one and not so good on the other," he replied.

"Knowing you, Larry, you probably failed both!" Kay sneered.

Larry grabbed a steak knife and stabbed her several times in the neck. Bob heard the commotion from his computer room and flung the door open. Larry stabbed him repeatedly in the chest until he died. Kay was still alive, but unconscious. Larry carried her outside and put her in the snow. After she came to, he dragged her back into the house and split her head with a maul. At 7 a.m. the next day, Larry called the police and said, "I think my parents are dead." It didn't take the police long to arrive at the Swartzes' house and determine that Larry had killed them.

Later, a police officer overheard Larry talking with a psychiatrist. "Why did you do it?" the psychiatrist asked.

"Frustration, revenge, to get them out of my life," Larry said.

This tragic true tale contains a harsh message for any of us considering becoming a parent. Physical abuse, verbal abuse, sexual abuse, and/or neglect can have a devastating psychological impact on children and, as a result, transform them into evildoers themselves.

Which of these risk factors is the most virulent? It's unclear at this juncture. Yet out of physical abuse, verbal abuse, sexual abuse, and neglect, physical abuse is the form of maltreatment most commonly experienced by youth who become serial killers. And evidence from a plethora of studies argues that a hostile, punitive parenting style can alchemize youngsters into bad individuals.

"We now know that if you beat the heck out of your child, you are pushing him or her in the direction of becoming violent," evildoer expert Michael Stone, MD, declares.

A chilling warning for all of us.

IF YOU COULD GET ONLY ONE THING RIGHT

Finally, there are also positive things that you can do to propel your children along the right moral path.

One of them is to try to instill empathy in them. Colorado researchers followed some 1,000 toddlers up to age 17 and found a strong link between a disregard for other people's pain early in life and the later development of antisocial behavior. Still other investigators have found that when parents explain to their children how a person in pain feels, it makes the children more caring in this regard. The entire focus of Kidsbridge Tolerance Center in New Jersey is helping parents, teachers, and caregivers learn to teach empathy to children. Founder Lynne Azarchi has published a guide to the process in *The Empathy Advantage.*

Another is to remain vigilant for any behaviors that suggest that they are heading in the wrong direction. Back during the 1970s, British scientists interviewed the parents of some 800 three-year-olds to learn whether the children engaged in any problem behaviors such as trouble concentrating, hyperactivity, attention-seeking, temper tantrums, or not minding. Then in 1993, the investigators traced, with the help of the British Criminal Records Office, which of the children, who were now young adults, had been convicted of crimes. Ten percent had. The investigators then looked to see whether there were any problem behaviors at age three that could be significantly linked with adult criminality. There were three, they found: disobeying, temper tantrums, and hyperactivity.

Something else to keep in mind, though, is that the presence of attention-deficit/hyperactivity disorder (ADHD) alone in childhood does not seem to herald antisocial behavior in adulthood. It has to be coupled with conduct disorder to do so, Sabine Herpertz, MD, of Aachen Technical University in Aachen, Germany and colleagues found in a study.

However, if you could do only one thing to keep your child from becoming an evildoer, it is probably this: Provide them with emotional warmth, but also set limits and enforce those limits firmly and consistently. Evidence backing this conclusion comes from a large body of research, notably two different seminal programs, both launched back during the 1970s—one by David Olds, PhD, of the University of Colorado at Denver and the other by Harvey Armstrong, MD, a child psychiatrist with the University of Toronto in Canada.

Olds' program was called the Nurse-Family Partnership. Its aim was to give first-born children from disadvantaged backgrounds a better start in life.

Nurses visited the mothers of those children before birth and also during the two years after birth. For example, while the mothers were pregnant, the nurses urged them to reduce their exposure to tobacco and alcohol, which can have adverse effects on brain development and subsequent behavior. Once the mothers gave birth, the nurses guided them on how to provide sensitive, responsive, and competent care for their babies and urged them to plan future pregnancies so that they could devote sufficient time to their babies, stay in school, and become economically self-sufficient. "Having economic stability in households is an important component in creating the right kinds of conditions for children to develop well," Olds told me during an interview.

In addition to developing this program, Olds and his team conducted studies to test its effectiveness.

In one study, they looked to see whether the program could reduce antisocial behaviors in the children whose mothers had participated. Four hundred women who awaited the birth of their first child served as subjects. Eighty-five percent were young, unmarried, or from low socioeconomic backgrounds. Half of the 400 women received the Nurse-Family Partnership intervention; the other half served as controls, receiving standard prenatal and well-child care in a clinic. Of the children born to the 400 women, 315 were available for follow-up during the next 15 years.

The children of mothers who had received the intervention experienced dramatically fewer arrests, convictions, and probation violations than did the children of controls. And as Olds and his team concluded in the October 14, 1998 *Journal of the American Medical Association,* "This program of prenatal and early-childhood home visitations by nurses can reduce reported serious antisocial behavior."

Subsequently, Olds and his team created a nonprofit organization known as the Nurse-Family Partnership National Service Office to help communities set up nurse-family partnerships. As of 2008, which was a decade later, these nurse-family partnerships were operating in 24 states and helping some 14,000 mothers and children annually. In fact, Olds traveled to Sweden that year to receive the 2008 Stockholm Prize in Criminology. The jury, which was composed of criminologists from various countries, praised Olds both for his innovative program and for the impact that it had had on crime reduction.

Since then, Olds has been working with investigators in Australia, Germany, and the Netherlands to determine whether the partnership concept might work in their countries as well.

And meanwhile, Armstrong has been advancing, in Canada, his own innovative program to prevent antisocial behavior.

During the 1970s, Armstrong was working in a family-court clinic as a child psychiatrist. He observed that many of the youngsters who came through the court system were psychologically more powerful than their parents. They would charm the judges and receive few penalties. The parents felt isolated, alone, intimidated, ashamed. Consequently, Armstrong helped found a nonprofit organization called "Parents for Youth: Helping and Supporting Parents of Difficult Youth." The goal of the organization was to teach parents how to set limits with their youngsters.

Indeed, findings from a large Canadian study supported this goal. It found that if parents rarely praise their child, the child is at only a slightly greater risk of becoming antisocial than is a youngster who receives lots of parental praise. In contrast, if parents are ineffective at parenting, their child is 37 times more likely to become antisocial than is a youngster with ineffective parents!

During the next 30 years, Armstrong's program gave assistance to more than a thousand parents. And the results were overall remarkably gratifying, he reports.

For instance, the stress level of parents when they entered the program was very high but started dropping after two or three sessions as the parents became more self-confident and more likely to take the risk of imposing consequences on their children if they did not obey. And as the parents started providing a firm, caring, supportive environment, their youngsters' egregious behaviors occurred less frequently.

"Most of the kids recovered, and most of the parents were satisfied with their kids' outcomes," Armstrong says.

CONCLUSION

Evildoing is not a subject for the faint of heart.

It is also contentious. One of my sources questioned the validity of some of the scientific results I present. Another argued that the information I include about violence is not comprehensive. (No, I omitted a number of categories of heinous acts.) Yet a third told me that while he had initially believed it appropriate to pass moral judgments on evildoing research findings, he has since decided that it is not. Science should remain untainted by interpretation, he argues. A fourth source said that he had "significant reservations about my use of the term "evil." He thinks of it as "a stigmatizing term rooted more in religion than in science and can even connote the presence of a supernatural force when trying to advance knowledge about mental experiences and their associated behaviors." He also contends that my definition of evildoers "as individuals who intentionally hurt others" is a "one-dimensional concept that does not do justice to the complexity of the matter. For example, according to that definition, all soldiers, boxers, self-defenders, those defending others, and per-haps even surgeons could potentially be defined as 'evildoers,' were consideration of their motives to be ignored...."

So feel free to vent and to disagree with me—but know that we can learn from the terrible things that have happened to others and bolster our own protection, and that of our children.

In the process of compiling this book, I have learned a lot about evildoing—things I hadn't known before. For example, some people show signs of depravity already in early childhood; women as well as men can be stalkers, and that stalkers, regardless of gender, can be dangerous; and while some of the most ghastly acts are committed by individuals with a severe mental illness, most vile acts are perpetrated by individuals who are sane.

What I have learned is also, hopefully, helping me treat other people better than I have in the past. For instance, I really didn't appreciate the extent of the damage that unkind words can have on people, so I'm now trying to evaluate the potential impact of any critical comments I want to make before I actually make them. Not easy!

And perhaps the most crucial thing I have learned from my book endeavor is that we are all flawed individuals—a mixture of both good and bad—and that redemption is possible for all of us.

May my book likewise profit you. Thank you and Godspeed!

SOURCES

CHAPTER ONE

Arehart-Treichel, Joan. An interview with Michael Stone, MD, on March 20, 2008.

Arehart-Treichel, Joan. An interview with John Young, MD, on May 21, 2001.

Arehart-Treichel, Joan. "Psychiatrist Helps Court Define 'Evil Behavior,'" *Psychiatric News*, June 15, 2001.

Stone, Michael, MD. One of the speakers at a symposium on "How Psychiatry Defines Evil," held at the 2001 annual meeting of the American Psychiatric Association.

Stone, Michael, MD. One of the speakers at a symposium on "Defining Evil: Clinical and Forensic Implications," held at the 2002 annual meeting of the American Psychiatric Association.

Stone, Michael, MD. *The Anatomy of Evil*, Prometheus Books, 2009.

Welner, Michael, MD. One of the speakers at a symposium on "How Psychiatry Defines Evil," held at the 2001 annual meeting of the American Psychiatric Association.

Welner, Michael, MD. One of the speakers at a symposium on "Defining Evil: Clinical and Forensic Implications," held at the 2002 annual meeting of the American Psychiatric Association.

CHAPTER TWO

Alvarez, Lizette. "British Doctor Who Killed 215 Hangs Himself," *The New York Times*, January 13, 2004.

Appelbaum, Paul, MD. "The Mind of the Murderer," *The Washington Post*, October 15, 2002.

Arehart-Treichel, Joan. An interview with Amin Muhammad Gadit, MD, on September 21, 2009.

Arehart-Treichel, Joan. "Don't Underestimate Dangerousness of Female Stalkers, Study Urges," *Psychiatric News*, February 1, 2002.

Arehart-Treichel, Joan. "Understanding Roots of Hostility Could Divert Its Expression," *Psychiatric News*, March 7, 2003.

Bender, Eve. "Expert Witness Describes Making of a Serial Killer," *Psychiatric News*, May 13, 2009.

Bowley, Graham and Lattman, Peter. "Madoff Lawsuits Are Headed for Court," *The New York Times*, December 13, 2010.

Butterfield, Fox. "Sniper Appears to Want to Create Fear, Not Pain," *The New York Times*, October 12, 2002.

Butterfield, Fox. "Sniper Doesn't Fit the Expected Profile," *The New York Times*, October 8, 2002.

Cannon, Angie. "Crime Stories of the Century," *US News & World Report*, December 6, 1999.

Dressing, Harald, MD. "Lifetime Prevalence and Impact of Stalking in a European Population," *The British Journal of Psychiatry*, August 2005.

Duenwald, Mary. "Who Would Abduct a Child? Previous Cases Offer Clues," *The New York Times*, August 27, 2002.

Duggan, Paul and Morse, Dan. "Tale of Grisly '97 Montgomery Killing Closes with Shots in an Israeli Prison," *The Washington Post*, February 25, 2014.

Eligon, John. "Wisconsin Suspect Killed Himself," *The New York Times*, August 8, 2012.

Hausman, Ken. "Classification Tries to Make Sense of Often Inexplicable Crime," *Psychiatric News*, December 20, 2002.

Healy, Jack. "Madoff Sentenced to 150 Years for Ponzi Scheme," *The New York Times*, June 29, 2009.

Hensley, Christopher. "The Effect of Inmates' Self-Reported Childhood and Adolescent Animal Cruelty," *The International Journal of Offender Therapy and Comparative Criminology*, April 2008.

Henriques, Diana and Baker, Al. "A Madoff Son Hangs Himself on Father's Arrest Anniversary. *The New York Times*, December 12, 2010.

Henriques, Diana. "Madoff Scheme Kept Rippling Outward, Across Borders," *The New York Times*, December 20, 2008.

Information about Eric Harris and Dillon Kliebold, aired by NBC TV "Dateline" on April 18, 2004.

Information about Bernie Madoff aired by PBS TV "Frontline" in 2009.

Information about Zacharia Oweiss, MD, published in *The Arab News* on August 24, 2001.

Information about Zacharia Oweiss, MD, aired by CBS TV on August 16, 2001.

Information about Robert Steinhauser in "Morderischer Abgang," published by *Der Spiegel* in Volume 18, 2002.

James, David et al. "Attacks on the British Royal Family: The Role of Psychotic Illness," *The Journal of the American Academy of Psychiatry and the Law*, April-June 2008.

Kovaleski, Serge and Ruane, Michael. "Hundreds of Leads to a Gunman," *The Washington Post*, October 7, 2002.

Kyle, Donald. "Inside the Roman Arena," *Odyssey*, January/February 2000.

Lehmann, Christine. "Stalker Classification Aids Diagnosis, Treatment," *Psychiatric News*, June 15, 2001.

Michaud, Stephen and Hazelwood, Roy. *The Evil That Men Do*, St. Martin's Paperbacks, 1998.

Moran, Mark. "Stalkers Inhabit a Reality All Their Own," *Psychiatric News*, November 5, 2004.

Ramsland, Katherine. "Evil, Part Two: The Heart of Darkness -- Reframing Evil," *The Crime Library*, March 19, 2002.

Schaffer, Michael and Cannon, Angie. "The Getaway Gunman," *US News & World Report*, October 28, 2002.

Schlesinger, Louis, PhD, et al. "Ritual and Signature in Serial Sexual Homicide," *The Journal of the American Academy of Psychiatry and the Law*, April-June 2010.

Snyder, David. "Potomac Doctor Held without Bond in Wife's Death," *The Washington Post*, August 16, 2001.

Snyder, David. "Potomac Gynecologist Charged in Wife's Death," *The Washington Post*, August 17, 2001.

Stone, Michael, MD. One of the speakers at a symposium on "Defining Evil: Clinical and Forensic Implications," held at the 2002 annual meeting of the American Psychiatric Association.

The Associated Press. "FBI Spy Sentenced to Life in Prison without Parole," *The New York Times*, May 10, 2002.

Wagner, Ario. "Doctor Charged with Killing Wife," *The Washington Times*, August 17, 2001.

CHAPTER THREE

Arehart-Treichel, Joan. An interview with John Young, MD, on May 17, 2001.

Arehart-Treichel, Joan. "Experts Explore Sadism, But Answers Remain Elusive," *Psychiatric News*, July 5, 2002.

Arehart-Treichel, Joan. "Psychiatrist Helps Court Define 'Evil Behavior'," *Psychiatric News*, June 15, 2001.

Goldstein, Rise, PhD, et al. "Lack of Remorse in Antisocial Personality Disorder," *Comprehensive Psychiatry*, July-August 2006.

Hansern, Mark. "Depravity Scale May Help Judges and Juries During Sentencing," published by The Depravity Scale.org blog, July 1, 2011.

Information about the prisoners in Riverbend Maximum Security Prison near Nashville, Tennessee. Aired by MSNBC TV on April 13, 2008.

Langman, Peter, PhD. *Why Kids Kill -- Inside the Minds of School Shooters,* Palgrave Macmillan, 2009.

Simon, Robert, MD. *Bad Men Do What Good Men Dream,* American Psychiatric Publishing, 2008.

Stone, Michael, MD. "Gradations of Antisociality and Responsivity to Psychosocial Therapies," Chapter Four in Psychotherapy for Personality Disorders, American Psychiatric Press, 2000.

Stone, Michael, MD. One of the speakers at a symposium on "Defining Evil: Clinical and Forensic Implications," held at the 2002 annual meeting of the American Psychiatric Association.

Stone, Michael, MD. One of the speakers at a symposium on "The Evil Standard: Milestones and Challenges," held at the 2003 annual meeting of the American Psychiatric Association.

Stone, Michael, MD. *The Anatomy of Evil,* Prometheus Books, 2009.

Tanay, Emanuel, MD. A letter to the editor regarding "Evil Behavior," *Psychiatric News,* September 21, 2001.

Tucker, Neely. "Giving Evil the Eye," *The Washington Post,* July 23, 2007.

Walters, Barbara. An interview with Senator Hilary Clinton about her life aired on ABC TV, June 8, 2003.

Welner, Michael, MD. A letter to the editor regarding "More on Depravity Scale," *Psychiatric News,* November 16, 2001.

Welner, Michael, MD. A response to Tanay's letter to the editor regarding "Evil Behavior," *Psychiatric News,* September 21, 2001.

Welner, Michael, MD. One of the speakers at a symposium on "Defining Evil: Clinical and Forensic Implications," held at the 2002 annual American Psychiatric Association.

Welner, Michael, MD. One of the speakers at a symposium on "The Evil Standard: Milestones and Challenges," held at the 2003 annual meeting of the American Psychiatric Association.

CHAPTER FOUR

Abushua'leh, Khalid, MD, and Abu-Akel, Ahmad, MD. "Association of Psychopathic Traits and Symptomatology with Violence in Patients with Schizophrenia," *Psychiatry Research*, August 30, 2006.

Alford, Roger. "Kentucky Man Admits to Murdering Parents," *The Washington Post*, October 9, 2002.

Anwar, Sophia, MD, et al. Is Arson the Crime Most Strongly Associated with Psychosis? —a National Case-Control Study of Arson Risk in Schizophrenia and Other Psychoses," *Schizophrenia Bulletin*, October 22, 2009.

Appelbaum, Paul, MD. "The Mind of the Murderer," *The Washington Post*, October 15, 2002.

Arehart-Treichel, Joan. An article about adult arsonists, *Psychiatric News*, October 2, 2009.

Arehart-Treichel, Joan. An interview with Jeffrey Swanson, PhD, on September 4, 2002.

Arehart-Treichel, Joan. "Attack on Former Beatle Linked to Health System Flaws," *Psychiatric News*, March 17, 2000.

Arehart-Treichel, Joan. Correspondence with David Kaczynski, the brother of Unibomber Ted Kaczynski, on January 25, 2008.

Arehart-Treichel, Joan. Correspondence with Pamela Taylor, MD, on November 9, 2004.

Arehart-Treichel, Joan. "Everyone Is in Danger of Committing Evil," *Psychiatric News*, June 15, 2001.

Arehart-Treichel, Joan. "Experts Narrow List of Violence Risk Factors," *Psychiatric News*, October 4, 2002.

Arehart-Treichel, Joan. "Mood, Substance Abuse Disorders Common Among Sex Offenders," *Psychiatric News*, May 21, 2004.

Arehart-Treichel, Joan. Correspondence with David Kaczynski, the brother of Unibomber Ted Kaczynski, on January 25, 2008.

Arehart-Treichel, Joan. Correspondence with Pamela Taylor, MD, on November 9, 2004.

Arehart-Treichel, Joan. "Psychiatrists Search for Links Between Religion, Illness," *Psychiatric News*, July 7, 2006.

Arehart-Treichel, Joan. "Researchers Explore Link Between Animal Cruelty, Personality Disorders," *Psychiatric News*, September 20, 2002.

Blamphin, John. "American Psychiatric Association Statement on the Insanity Defense and Mental Illness," a news release released by the American Psychiatric Association on March 15, 2002.

Buckley, Peter, MD. "Insight and Its Relationship to Violent Behavior in Patients with Schizophrenia," The American Journal of Psychiatry, September 2004.

Cartwright, Rosalind, PhD. "Sleepwalking Violence: A Sleep Disorder, a Legal Dilemma, and a Psychological Challenge," *The American Journal of Psychiatry*, July 2004.

Cold, Jeremy, MD, and Ullrich, Simone, PhD. "Antisocial Personality Disorder Is on a Continuum with Psychopathy," *Comprehensive Psychiatry*, December 21, 2009.

Cold, Jeremy, MD. "The Relationship Between Delusions and Violence," *JAMA Psychiatry*, March 6, 2013.

Duggan, Paul. "Texas Mother Convicted of Murder," *The Washington Post*, March 13, 2002.

Easton, Pam. "Yates Spared From Death Penalty," *The Washington Times*, March 16, 2002.

Ferranti, Jessica, MD, et al. "Characteristics of Female Homicide Offenders Found Not Guilty by Reason of Insanity," *The Journal of the American Academy of Psychiatry and the Law*, October-December 2013.

Fountain, John. "Verdict Near on Mother of Dead Children," *The New York Times*, December 19, 2001.

Hausman, Ken. "Court Still Clarifying Rules for Executing Mentally Ill," *Psychiatric News*, May 18, 2007.

Herold, Eve. "American Psychiatric Association Responds to NRA Comments," a news release released by the American Psychiatric Association on December 23, 2012.

Information about Andrea Yates from an interview with her mother aired on NBC TV "Nightly News," August 13, 2001.

Information about Andrea Yates from a CBS TV "Sixty Minutes" segment aired on December 9, 2001.

Information about Antisocial Personality Disorder in The Diagnostic and Statistical Manual of Mental Disorders Fourth Edition Text Revision (DSM-IV-TR) , published by the American Psychiatric Association in 2000.

Information about Hitler and Stalin aired on the History Channel, Decembr 11, 2003.

Information about Narcissistic Personality Disorder in *The Diagnostic and Statistical Manual of Mental Disorders Fourth Edition Text Revision* (DSM-IV-TR), published by the American Psychiatric Association in 2000.

Information about Paranoid Personality Disorder in *The Diagnostic and Statistical Manual of Mental Disorders Fourth Edition Text Revision* (DSM-IV-TR), published by the American Psychiatric Association in 2000.

Johnson, Sally, PhD. "Psychological Evaluation of Theodore Kaczynski," aired on Court TV News, January 28, 2008.

Jones, Jack. "Death of a Beatle," aired on Court TV Online, February 5, 2004.

Kendell, R.E. "The Distinction Between Personality Disorder and Mental Illness," *The British Journal of Psychiatry*, February 2002.

Klein, Rachel. "Clinical and Functional Outcome of Childhood Attention-Deficit/Hyperactivity Disorder 33 Years Later," *The Archives of General Psychiatry*, October 15, 2012.

Kravitz, Howard, DO. "A Cross-Sectional Study of Psychosocial and Criminal Factors Associated with Arrest in Mentally Ill Female Detainees," *The Journal of the American Academy of Psychiatry and the Law*, July-September 2002.

Kupersanin, Eve. "High Court Won't Hear Appeal of Forced Medication Case," *Psychiatric News*, January 18, 2002.

Langman, Peter, PhD. *Why Kids Kill -- Inside the Minds of School Shooters*, Palgrave Macmillan, 2009.

Liptak, Adam. "State Can Make Inmate Sane Enough to Execute," *The New York Times*, February 2, 2003.

Lying by adults -- a session at the American Psychoanalytic Association meeting held in January 2010.

Malmquist, Carl, MD. *Homicide: A Psychiatric Perspective*, American Psychiatric Press, 1996.

Miraglia, Richard and Hall, Donna, PhD. "The Effect of Length of Hospitalization on Re-arrest Among Insanity Plea Acquittees," *The Journal of the American Academy of Psychiatry and the Law*, October-December 2011.

Modestin, J. "Criminal and Violent Behavior in Schizophrenia Patients: an Overview," *Psychiatry and Clinical Neuroscience*, December 1998.

Moran, Mark. "Antisocial Personality Disorder: When Is It Treatable?" *Psychiatric News*, January 2, 2004.

Moran, Mark. "Findings of Landmark Study Still Provoke Heated Debate," *Psychiatric News*, February 1, 2008.

Moran, Mark. "Insanity Standards May Vary, But Plea Rarely Succeeds," *Psychiatric News*, April 19, 2002.

Moran, Mark. "Psychiatrists Disagree About Crime-Schizophrenia Link," *Psychiatric News*, May 21, 2004.

Moran, Mark. "Small Percentage of Violent Crime Attributable to Mental Illness," *Psychiatric News*, September 1, 2006.

Moran, Mark. "Yates Case Puts Mental Illness in Media Spotlight," *Psychiatric News*, April 19, 2002.

O'Reilly, Bill. An interview with Michael Welner, MD, aired on Fox TV's "The O'Reilly Factor," April 18, 2007.

Putkonen, Hanna, MD. "Risk of Repeat Offending Among Violent Female Offenders with Psychotic and Personality Disorders," *The American Journal of Psychiatry*, May 2003.

Repo, E. "Criminal and Psychiatric Histories of Finnish Arsonists," *Acta Psychiatrica Scandinavica*, April 1997.

Schlesinger, Louis, PhD, et al. "Ritual and Signature in Serial Sexual Homicide," *The Journal of the American Academy of Psychiatry and the Law*, April-June 2010.

Sentementes, Gus. "Cannibalism Suspect Gets Support From East Baltimore Church," *The Baltimore Sun*, June 4, 2012.

Simon, Robert, MD. Bad Men Do What Good Men Dream, American Psychiatric Publishing, 2008.

Sinclair, Leslie. "Evidence Supports Link Between Schizophrenia, Violent Crime," *Psychiatric News*, September 2, 2011.

Stone, Michael, MD. "Gradations of Antisociality and Responsivity to Psychosocial Therapies," Chapter Four, *Psychotherapy for Personality Disorders*, edited by John Gunderson, MD, et al, American Psychiatric Press, 2000.

Stone, Michael, MD. One of the speakers at a symposium on "How Psychiatry Defines Evil," held at the 2001 annual meeting of the American Psychiatric Association.

Stone, Michael, MD. "Serial Sexual Homicide: Biological, Psychological, and Sociological Aspects," *The Journal of Personality Disorders*, February 2001.

Stone, Michael, MD. *The Anatomy of Evil*, Prometheus Books, 2009.

Welner, Michael, MD. One of the speakers at a symposium on "How Psychiatry Defines Evil," held at the 2001 annual meeting of the American Psychiatric Association.

White, Erin. "Inside the Minds of Murderers," a press release released by Northwestern University on June 27, 2013.

Winsper, Catherine, PhD. "Pathways to Violent Behavior During First-Episode Psychosis," *JAMA Psychiatry*, October 2, 2013.

Yan, Jun. "Child Behavior Problems May Signal Pathway to Violence in Schizophrenia," *Psychiatric News*, September 7, 2007.

CHAPTER FIVE

Anon. "Crime Genes: The Danish Adoption Studies," *Gene Letter*, November 1, 1996.

Anon. "Laci Peterson press conference information released by the Modesto, California police on April 18, 2003.

Anon. "Laci Peterson: A Fateful 24 Hours," published by www.KTVU.com, February 16-17, 2003.

Anon. "Police: Laci Peterson Is Victim of Violence," published by www.CNN.com, March 6, 2003.

Anon. "Study Reveals Specific Gene in Adolescent Men with Delinquent Peers," Newswise, October 1, 2008.

Arehart-Treichel, Joan. An interview with S. Alexandra Burt, PhD, on May 14, 2008.

Arehart-Treichel, Joan. An interview with Michael Stone, MD, on March 20, 2008.

Arehart-Treichel, Joan. "Boys without Siblings May Be at Greater Risk for Antisocial Behavior," *Psychiatric News*, June 15, 2001.

Arehart-Treichel, Joan. "Can Better Diet Prevent Antisocial Behavior?" *Psychiatric News*, May 2, 2003.

Arehart-Treichel, Joan. "Conduct Disorder, Alcoholism May Share Genetic Link," *Psychiatric News*, March 5, 2004.

Arehart-Treichel, Joan. Correspondence with Tanya Button, PhD, on April 13, 2008.

Arehart-Treichel, Joan. Correspondence with Brian D'Onofrio, PhD, on July 6, 2007.

Arehart-Treichel, Joan. Correspondence with Debra Foley, PhD, on September 3, 2004.

Arehart-Treichel, Joan. Correspondence with Frank Verhulst, MD, on March 13, 2008.

Arehart-Treichel, Joan. "Fine Line Separates Personality Quirks From Personality Disorder," *Psychiatric News,* August 2, 2002.

Arehart-Treichel, Joan. "Gene Variant, Family Factors Can Raise Conduct Disorder Risk," *Psychiatric News*, September 3, 2004.

Arehart-Treichel, Joan. "Gene Variant in Abused Boys Linked to Antisocial Behavior," *Psychiatric News*, December 1, 2006.

Arehart-Treichel, Joan. "Multiple Factors at Root of Antisocial Behavior," *Psychiatric News*, August 1, 2008.

Arehart-Treichel, Joan. "Psychosocial Factors Outweigh Genes in Development of Antisocial Behavior," *Psychiatric News*, November 4, 2005.

Arehart-Treichel, Joan. "Scientific Advances Changing Forensic Psychiatry," *Psychiatric News*, July 19, 2013.

Arehart-Treichel, Joan. "Smoking When Pregnant Tied to Risk That Offspring Will Be Criminals," *Psychiatric News*, January 17, 2002.

Beaven, Stephen and Crombie, Noelle. "Second Teen Alleges Weaver Assault," *The Oregonian*, August 28, 2002.

Beaver, Kevin, PhD. "Monoamine Oxidase A Genotype Is Associated with Gang Membership and Weapon Use," *Comprehensive Psychiatry*, May 5, 2009.

Blair, James, PhD. A commentary. "Disregard for Others: Empathic Dysfunction or Emotional Volatility? The Relationship with Future Antisocial Behavior -- Reflections on Rhee et al (2013)," *The Journal of Child Psychology and Psychiatry*, February 2013.

Bower, Bruce. "Violent Developments," *Science News*, May 27, 2006.

Brennan, Patricia, PhD. "Relationship of Maternal Smoking During Pregnancy with Criminal Arrest and Hospitalization for Substance Abuse in Male and Female Adult Offspring," *The American Journal of Psychiatry*, January 2002.

Brunner, H.G., PhD. "Abnormal Behavior Associated with a Point Mutation in the Structural Gene for Monoamine Oxidase A," *Science*, October 22, 1993.

Cadoret, Remi, MD. "Genetic - Environmental Interactions in the Genesis of Aggressivity and Conduct Disorder," *The Archives of General Psychiatry*, November 1995.

Caspi, Avshelom, MD, et al. "Role of Genotype in the Cycle of Violence in Maltreated Children," *Science*, August 2, 2002.

Cohen, Lisa, PhD, et al. "Childhood Sexual History of 20 Male Pedophiles versus 24 Male Healthy Controls," *The Journal of Nervous and Mental Disease*, 2002.

Cohen, Patricia. "Genetic Basis for Crime: A New Look," *The New York Times*, June 20, 2011.

Comings, David, MD. "Dopamine D2 Receptor (DRD2) Gene and Susceptibility to Posttraumatic Stress Disorder: A Study and Replication," *Biological Psychiatry*, 1996.

Disney, Elizabeth, PhD, et al. "Strengthening the Case: Prenatal Alcohol Exposure Is Associated with Increase Risk for Conduct Disorder," *Pediatrics*, December 2008.

D'Onofrio, Brian, PhD, et al. "Intergenerational Transmission of Childhood Conduct Problems," *The Archives of General Psychiatry*, July 2007.

Eggen, Dan. "Grief, Questions Linger in Oregon Slayings," *The Washington Post*, August 28, 2002.

Feinberg, Mark, PhD, et al. "Parenting and Adolescent Antisocial Behavior and Depression," *The Archives of General Psychiatry*, April 2007.

Fergusson, David, PhD, et al. "Exposure to Single Parenthood in Childhood and Later Mental Health, Educational, Economic, and Criminal Behavior Outcomes," *The Archives of General Psychiatry*, September 2007.

Ford, Charles, MD. Lies! Lies! Lies! -- the Psychology of Deceit, American Psychiatric Press, 1996.

Friedland, Steven. "The Criminal Law Implications of the Human Genome Project," *The Kentucky Law Journal*, 1997.

Friedman, Richard, MD. "Scientific Observations," *Science News*, August 14, 2010.

Gao, Y.U. "Early Maternal and Paternal Bonding, Childhood Physical Abuse, and Adult Psychopathic Personality," *Psychological Medicine*, September 15, 2009.

Gaulibaud du Fort, G. "Spouse Similarity for Antisocial Behavior in the General Population," *Psychological Medicine*, November 2002.

Gotz, M.J., MD., et al. "Criminality and Antisocial Behavior in Unselected Men with Sex Chromosome Abnormalities," *Psychological Medicine*, July 29, 1999.

Information about Conduct Disorder in *The Diagnostic and Statistical Manual of Mental Disorders Fourth Edition Text Revision* (DSM-IV-TR), published by the American Psychiatric Association in 2000.

Information about Hitler and Stalin aired on The History Channel on December 11, 2003.

Jaffee, Sara, PhD, et al. "Life with (or without) Father: The Benefits of Living with Two Biological Parents Depend on the Father's Antisocial Behavior," *Child Development*, January/February 2003.

Kemppainen, Liisa, MD, et al. "The One-Child Family and Violent Criminality: A 31-Year Follow-up Study of the Northern Finland 1966 Birth Cohort," *The American Journal of Psychiatry*, June 2001.

Kendler, Kenneth, MD, et al. "Familial Influences on Conduct Disorder Reflect Two Genetic Factors and One Shared Environmental Factor," *The Archives of General Psychiatry*, November 2012.

Kendler, Kenneth, MD. "Genetic Epidemiology in Psychiatry," *The Archives of General Psychiatry,* November 1995.

Kim-Cohen, Julia, PhD, et al. "MAOA, Maltreatment, and Gene-Environment Interaction Predicting Children's Mental Health: New Evidence and a Meta-analysis," *Molecular Psychiatry*, October 2006.

Kim-Cohen, Julia, PhD, et al. "The Caregiving Environment Provided to Children by Depressed Mothers with or without an Antisocial History," *The American Journal of Psychiatry*, June 2006.

Kramer, Andrew. "Human Remains Identified as Missing 12-Year-Old Oregon Girl," *The Boston Globe,* August 26, 2002.

Kramer, Andrew. "Weaver's Father Buried in Yard in 1981," *The Seattle Times*, August 29, 2002.

Langley, Kate, PhD, et al. "Genotype Link with Extreme Antisocial Behavior," *The Archives of General Psychiatry*, December 2010.

Levin, Aaron. "As Genetic Data Increase, How Will Courts Respond?" *Psychiatric News*, December 7, 2012.

Li, Dawei, PhD, et al. "Association of COL25A1 with Comorbid Antisocial Personality Disorder and Substance Dependence," *Biological Psychiatry*, April 15, 2012.

Liu, Jianghong, PhD, et al. "Malnutrition at Age 3 Years and Externalizing Behavior Problems at Ages 8, 11, and 17 Years," *The American Journal of Psychiatry*, November 2004.

Michaud, Stephen and Hazelwood, Roy. *The Evil That Men Do*, St. Martin's Paperbacks, 1998.

Moran, Mark. "Antisocial Personality Disorder: When Is It Treatable?" *Psychiatric News*, January 2, 2004.

Moran, Mark. "Jury Still Out on Impact of Genes on Trial Verdicts," *Psychiatric News*, November 3, 2006.

Moran, Mark. "Mind-Brain Dichotomy Irrelevant in Personality Disorders, Gabbard Says," *Psychiatric News*, July 18, 2004.

New, Antonia, MD, et al. "Genetic Polymorphisms and Aggression," Chapter 12 in *Molecular Genetics and the Human Personality*, edited by Jonathan Benjamin, MD, et al, American Psychiatric Association Publishing, 2002.

Paris, Joel, MD. Nature and Nurture in Psychiatry, American Psychiatric Press, 1999.

Redden, Jim. "Portland Tribune: Eerie Parallels Emerge in Oregon City Probe, published by www.MSNBC.com , August 23, 2002.

Scourfield, Jane, PhD, et al. "Conduct Problems in Childhood and Adolescents," *The Archives of General Psychiatry*, May 2004.

Simon, Robert, MD. *Bad Men Do What Good Men Dream*, American Psychiatric Publishing, 2008.

Steinberg, Annie, MD. "Youth Hate Crimes: Identification, Prevention, and Intervention," *The American Journal of Psychiatry*, May 2003.

Stone, Michael, MD. One of the speakers at a symposium on "Defining Evil: Clinical and Forensic Implications," held at the 2002 annual meeting of the American Psychiatric Association.

Stone, Michael, MD. One of the speakers at a symposium on "How Psychiatry Defines Evil," held at the 2001 annual meeting of the American Psychiatric Association.

Stone, Michael, MD. "Serial Sexual Homicide: Biological, Psychological, and Sociological Aspects," The Journal of Personality Disorders, February 2001.

Stone, Michael, MD. *The Anatomy of Evil*, Prometheus Books, 2009.

Thornberry, Terence, PhD. "The Impact of Parental Stressors on the Intergenerational Transmission of Antisocial Behavior," *The Journal of Youth and Adolescence*, September 30, 2008.

Verhulst, Frank, MD. "The 14-Year Prediction of Antisocial Behavior," Chapter 11, *Developmental Psychopathology and Wellness*, edited by James Hudziak, MD, American Psychiatric Publishing, 2008.

Wamboldt, Marianne, MD, and Reiss, David, MD. "Explorations of Parenting Environments in the Evolution of Psychiatric Problems in Children," *The American Journal of Psychiatry*, June 2006.

Welner, Michael, MD. One of the speakers at a symposium on "Defining Evil: Clinical and Forensic Implications," held at the 2002 annual meeting of the American Psychiatric Association.

Welner, Michael, MD. One of the speakers at a symposium on "How Psychiatry Defines Evil," held at the 2001 annual meeting of the American Psychiatric Association.

Zohsel, Katrin, PhD, et al. "Mothers' Prenatal Stress and Their Children's Antisocial Outcomes -- a Moderating Role for the Dopamine D4 Receptor (DRD4) Gene," *The Journal of Child Psychology and Psychiatry*, September 14, 2013.

CHAPTER SIX

Aluja, Anton, PhD, and Garcia, Luis, PhD. "Role of Sex Hormone-binding Globulin in the Relationship Between Sex Hormones and

Antisocial and Aggressive Personality in Inmates," *Psychiatry Research*, 2007.

Anon. An interview with Adrian Raine, PhD, in *New Scientist*, May 13, 2000.

Anon. "Olfactory Abilities and Psychopathy: Higher Psychopathy Scores Are Associated with Poorer Odor Discrimination and Identification," *Chemosensory Perception*, September 2012.

Anon. "Testosterone's Family Ties," *Science News*, January 18, 2003.

Anon. "Violence in Certain Men Linked to Gray Matter Deficits," *Psychiatric News*, March 3, 2000.

Arehart-Treichel, Joan. "Abnormal Brain Region Characterizes Those with Psychopathy," *Psychiatric News*, October 16, 2009.

Arehart-Treichel, Joan. "ADHD + Conduct Disorder May Signal Trouble Ahead," *Psychiatric News*, February 1, 2002.

Arehart-Treichel, Joan. An interview with Michael Stone, MD, on March 20, 2008.

Arehart-Treichel, Joan. "Brain Region's Dopamine Levels Linked to Psychopathy Trait," *Psychiatric News*, May 7, 2010.

Arehart-Treichel, Joan. "Evidence Builds for Prefrontal Cortex Abnormality in Conduct Disorder," *Psychiatric News*, April 5, 2002.

Arehart-Treichel, Joan. "Further Study Urged of Brain Findings in Psychopathy," *Psychiatric News*, July 20, 2012.

Arehart-Treichel, Joan. "LH and FSH Appear to Predict Sexual Offending," *Psychiatric News*, December 2013.

Arehart-Treichel, Joan. "Multiple Factors at Root of Antisocial Behavior," *Psychiatric News*, August 1, 2008.

Balaban, E. et al. "Mean Genes and the Biology of Aggression: a Critical Review of Recent Animal and Human Research," *The Journal of Neurogenetics*, December 1996.

Bender, Eve. "Understanding Aggression: It's Largely in the Planning," *Psychiatric News*, December 5, 2003.

Brewer-Smyth et al. "Physical and Sexual Abuse, Salivary Cortisol, and Neurologic Correlates of Violent Criminal Behavior in Female Prison Inmates," *Biological Psychiatry,* July 2, 2003.

Buchsbaum, Monte, MD. "Frontal Cortex Function," *The American Journal of Psychiatry,* December 2004.

Dads, Mark, PhD, et al. "Reduced Eye Gaze Explains 'Fear Blindness' in Childhood Psychopathic Traits," *The Journal of the American Academy of Child & Adolescent Psychiatry,* April 2008.

Decety, Jean, PhD, et al. "Brain Response to Empathy-Eliciting Scenarios Involving Pain in Incarcerated Individuals with Psychopathy," *JAMA Psychiatry,* April 24, 2013.

Fairchild, Graeme, PhD, et al. "Brain Structure Abnormalities in Adolescent Girls with Conduct Disorder," *The Journal of Child Psychology and Psychiatry,* January 2013.

Fairchild, Graeme, PhD, et al. "Facial Expression Recognition, Fear Conditioning, and Startle Modulation in Female Subjects with Conduct Disorder," *Biological Psychiatry,* May 6, 2010.

Fairchild, Graeme, PhD, et al. "Fear Conditioning and Affective Modulation of Startle Reflex in Male Adolescents with Early-Onset or Adolescence-Onset Conduct Disorder and Healthy Control Subjects," *Biological Psychiatry,* September 3, 2007.

Herpertz, Sabine, MD, et al. "Emotion in Criminal Offenders with Psychopathy and Borderline Personality Disorder," *The Archives of General Psychiatry,* August 2001.

Herpertz, Sabine, MD, et al. "Similar Autonomic Responsivity in Boys with Conduct Disorder and Their Fathers," *Journal of the American Academy of Child & Adolescent Psychiatry,* April 2007.

Hodgins, Sheilagh, PhD, et al. "Obstetric Complications, Parenting, and Risk of Criminal Behavior," *The Archives of General Psychiatry,* August 2001.

Information about Adrian Raine, PhD, and his group's research. From the University of Southern California Neuroscience Graduate Program in 2001.

Information about Joseph Vacher in the film "Joseph Vacher -- the Shepherd Killer," aired by MHz International Mysteries on January 28, 2017.

Information about low serotonin levels in temper-prone individuals. From *The Diagnostic and Statistical Manual of Mental Disorders Fourth Edition Text Revision* (DSM-IV-TR), published by the American Psychiatric Association in 2000, p. 664.

Kendell, R.E., PhD. "The Distinction Between Personality Disorder and Mental Illness," *The British Journal of Psychiatry*, February 2002.

Kingston, Drew, PhD, et al. "The Role of Central and Peripheral Hormones in Sexual and Violent Recidivism in Sex Offenders," *The Journal of the American Academy of Psychiatry and the Law*, October - December 2012.

Lewis, Dorothy, MD, et al. "Six Adoptees Who Murdered: Neuropsychiatric Vulnerabilities and Characteristics of Biological and Adoptive Parents," *The Journal of the American Academy of Psychiatry and the Law*, October-December 2001.

Lozier, Leah, et al. "Mediation of the Relationship Between Callous-Unemotional Traits and Proactive Aggression by Amygdala Response to Fear Among Children with Conduct Problems," *JAMA Psychiatry*, March 26, 2014.

Malmquist, Carl, MD. *Homicide: A Psychiatric Perspective*, American Psychiatric Publishing, 2006.

Mendez, Mario, MD, PhD. "The Unique Predisposition to Criminal Violations in Frontotemporal Dementia," *The Journal of the American Academy of Psychiatry and the Law*, July-September 2010.

Narayan, Veena et al. "Regional Cortical Thinning in Subjects with Violent Antisocial Personality Disorder or Schizophrenia," *The American Journal of Psychiatry*, September 2007.

Orellana, Gricel, MD, PhD, et al. "Psychosis-Related Matricide Associated with a Lesion of the Ventromedial Prefrontal Cortex," *The Journal of the American Academy of Psychiatry and the Law*, July-September 2013.

Ortiz, Jame and Raine, Adrian, PhD. "Heart Rate Level and Antisocial Behavior in Children and Adolescents: A Meta-analysis," *The Journal of the American Academy of Child and Adolescent Psychiatry*, February 2004.

Pardini, Dustin, PhD, et al. "Lower Amygdala Volume in Men Is Associated with Childhood Aggression, Early Psychopathic Traits, and Future Violence," *Biological Psychiatry*, May 6, 2013.

Paris, Joel, MD. *Nature and Nurture in Psychiatry*, American Psychiatric Press, 1999.

Rilling, James, PhD. "Neural Correlates of Social Cooperation and Non-cooperation as a Function of Psychopathy," *Biological Psychiatry*, 2006.

Sabbatini, Renato, PhD. "The Psychopath's Brain," *Brain and Mind Magazine*, 1998.

Schiffer, Boris, PhD, et al. "Disentangling Structural Brain Alterations Associated with Violent Behavior From Those Associated with Substance Use Disorders," *The Archives of General Psychiatry*, October 2011.

Silva, J. Arturo, MD. "Commentary: The Forensic Psychiatry of Frontotemporal Dementia," *The Journal of the American Academy of Psychiatry and the Law*, July-September 2010.

Smith, Abbe, JD. "Commentary: Six Adoptees Who Murdered -- Implications for Trial and Sentencing," *The Journal of the American Academy of Psychiatry and the Law*, October-December 2001.

Stone, Michael, MD. *The Anatomy of Evil*, Prometheus Books, 2009.

Sutliff, Usha. "USC Study Finds Faulty Wiring in Psychopaths." A press release issued by EurekAlert on March 10, 2004.

Yang, Yaling, et al. "Prefrontal White Matter in Pathological Liars," *The British Journal of Psychiatry*, October 2005.

Yang, Yaling, et al. "Volume Reduction in Prefrontal Gray Matter in Unsuccessful Criminal Psychopaths," *Biological Psychiatry*, May 15, 2005.

Van Os, Jim, MD, PhD, et al. "A Prospective Twin Study of Birth Weight Discordance and Child Problem Behavior," *Biological Psychiatry*, October 15, 2001.

CHAPTER SEVEN

Arehart-Treichel, Joan. An interview with Michael Stone, MD, on March 20, 2008.

Arehart-Treichel, Joan. "Can Pathological Liars Blame It on the Brain?" *Psychiatric News*, November 18, 2005.

Arehart-Treichel, Joan. Correspondence with Fred Berlin, MD, PhD, on March 26, 2013.

Arehart-Treichel, Joan. Correspondence with Park Dietz, MD, PhD, on March 28, 2013.

Arehart-Treichel, Joan. Correspondence with Robert Granacher, Jr, MD, in 2013.

Arehart-Treichel, Joan. "Genes, Neuroscience, and Free Will," *Psychiatric News*, June 5, 2009.

Arehart-Treichel, Joan. "Scientific Advances Changing Forensic Psychiatry," *Psychiatric News*, July 19, 2013.

Bender, Eve. "Death-Penalty Opponents Cite Teens' Immature Brains," *Psychiatric News*, November 15, 2002.

Fried, L. "Mellansjo School-Home. Psychopathic Children Admitted 1928-1940, Their Social Adaptation Over 30 Years: A Longitudinal Prospective Follow-up," *Acta Paedriatrica Supplement*, April 1995.

Friedland, Steven. "The Criminal Law Implications of the Human Genome Project," *The Kentucky Law Journal*, 1997.

Friedman, Richard, MD. "Beyond Anger: Studying the Subconscious Nature of Rage," *The New York Times*, November 12, 2002.

Hagerty, Barbara. "Can Your Genes Make You Murder?" Aired by National Public Radio on July 1, 2010.

Herbert, Wray. "How the Nature Versus Nurture Debate Shapes Public Policy -- and Our View of Ourselves," U.S. News & World Report, April 21, 1997.

Malmquist, Carl, MD. Homicide: A Psychiatric Perspective, Second Edition, American Psychiatric Publishing, 2006.

Mendez, Mario, MD, PhD. "The Unique Predisposition to Criminal Violations in Frontotemporal Dementia," *The Journal of the American Academy of Psychiatry and the Law*, July-September 2010.

Moran, Mark. "Antisocial Personality Disorder: When Is It Treatable?" *Psychiatric News*, November 3, 2006.

Motluk, Alison. An interview with Adrian Raine, PhD, published in *New Scientist*, May 13, 2000.

Paris, Joel, MD. Prescriptions for the Mind -- a Critical View of Contemporary Psychiatry, Oxford University Press, 2008.

Simon, Robert, MD. *Bad Men Do What Good Men Dream*, American Psychiatric Publishing, 2008.

Spence, Sean, MD. "Prefrontal White Matter -- the Tissue of Lies," *The British Journal of Psychiatry*, October 2005.

Staub, Ervin, PhD. *The Psychology of Good and Evil*, Cambridge University Press, 2003.

Stone, Michael, MD. One of the speakers at a symposium on "Defining Evil -- Clinical and Forensic Implications," held at the 2002 annual meeting of the American Psychiatric Association.

Stone, Michael, MD. "Serial Sexual Homicide: Biological, Psychological, and Sociological Aspects," The Journal of Personality Disorders, February 2001.

Stone, Michael, MD. One of the speakers at a symposium on "Defining Evil -- Clinical and Forensic Implications," held at the 2002 annual meeting of the American Psychiatric Association.

Yang, Yaling et al. "Prefrontal White Matter in Pathological Liars," *The British Journal of Psychiatry*, October 2005.

CHAPTER EIGHT

Anon. A press release about conduct disorder demographics released by the American Academy of Child & Adolescent Psychiatry on March 31, 2008.

Anon. "France's Worst Serial Killers?" published by World News Review on May 26, 2008.

Anon. "French Serial Killer Couple Handed Life Sentences," published by www.CNN.com on May 28, 2008.

Anon. Information about Dennis Hastert aired by CBS TV Evening News, April 27, 2016.

Anon. Information about Dennis Hastert reported in *The New York Times* on July 18, 2017.

Arehart-Treichel, Joan. "Adult Criminology May Be Rooted in Troubling Childhood Behaviors," *Psychiatric News*, January 4, 2002.

Arehart-Treichel, Joan. An article about adult arsonists, Psychiatric News, October 2, 2009.

Arehart-Treichel, Joan. An interview with Joel Paris, MD, on April 26, 2002.

Arehart-Treichel, Joan. An interview with Jeffrey Swanson, PhD, on September 4, 2002.

Arehart-Treichel, Joan. "Brain Abnormalities Found in Girls with Conduct Disorder," Psychiatric News, 2013.

Arehart-Treichel, Joan. Correspondence with Graeme Fairchild, MD, on January 21, 2013.

Arehart-Treichel, Joan. Correspondence with William Pollack, MD, on April 3, 2008.

Arehart-Treichel, Joan. "Don't Underestimate Dangerousness of Female Stalkers, Study Urges," *Psychiatric News*, February 1, 2002.

Arehart-Treichel, Joan. "Psychiatrist Helps Court Define 'Evil Behavior,'" *Psychiatric News*, June 15, 2001.

Barakat, Matthew. "Virginia Teen on Trial for Dad's Murder," *The Washington Post*, October 6, 2002.

Bell, Rachael. "Michel Fourniret Serial Killer, published by www.trutv. com on May 29, 2008.

Blair, James, PhD. A commentary. "Disregard for Others: Empathic Dysfunction or Emotional Volatility? The Relationship with Future Antisocial Behavior -- Reflections on Rhee et al (2013)," *The Journal of Child Psychology and Psychiatry*, February 2013.

Bledsoe, Jerry. *Before He Wakes: A True Story of Money, Marriage, Sex, and Murder*, Onyx Books, 1996.

Bourget, Dominique, MD. "Parricide: A Comparative Study of Matricide Versus Patricide," The Journal of the American Academy of Psychiatry and the Law, July-September 2007.

Burt, S. Alexandra, PhD. "Does Marriage Inhibit Antisocial Behavior?" *The Archives of General Psychiatry*, December 2010.

Chen, Y.-H. et al. "Firesetting in Adolescence and Being Aggressive, Shy, and Rejected by Peers: New Epidemiologic Evidence From a National Sample Survey," *The Journal of the American Academy of Psychiatry and the Law*, January-March 2003.

Daugherty, Scott and Sauers, Elisha. "Suspect's Neighbors Stunned," The Evening Capital, June 11, 2009.

Dressing, Harold, MD. "Lifetime Prevalence and Impact of Stalking in a European Population," *The British Journal of Psychiatry*, August 2005.

Duenwald, Mary. "Who Would Abduct a Child? Previous Cases Offer Clues," *The New York Times*, August 27, 2002.

Duggan, Paul and Morse, Dan. "Tale of Grisly '97 Montgomery Killing Closes with Shots in an Israeli Prison," *The Washington Post*, February 24, 2014.

Eaton, Joe. "The New Dealers," *The AARP Bulletin*, June 2017.

Ferranti, Jessica, MD, et al. "Characteristics of Female Homicide Offenders Found Not Guilty by Reason of Insanity," *The Journal of the American Academy of Psychiatry and the Law*, October-December 2013.

Foderaro, Lisa. "Private Moment Made Public, Then a Fatal Jump," The New York Times, September 30, 2010.

Ford, Charles, MD. *Lies! Lies! Lies! -- the Psychology of Deceit*, American Psychiatric Press, 1996.

Frierson, Richard, MD. "Biosocial Traits of Juvenile Murderers," reported at a meeting of the American Academy of Psychiatry and the Law in 2001.

Gurian, Elizabeth. "Female Serial Murderers: Directions for Future Research on a Hidden Population," *The International Journal of Offender Therapy and Comparative Criminology*, November 12, 2009.

Information about Antisocial Personality Disorder in The Diagnostic and Statistical Manual of Mental Disorders Fourth Edition Text Revision (DSM-IV-TR), published by the American Psychiatric Association in 2000.

Information about Conduct Disorder in The Diagnostic and Statistical Manual of Mental Disorders Fourth Edition Text Revision (DSM-IV-TR), published by the American Psychiatric Association in 2000.

Keenan, Kate, PhD, and Wakschlag, Lauren, PhD. "Are Oppositional Defiant and Conduct Disorder Symptoms Normative Behaviors in Preschoolers? A Comparison of Referred and Nonreferred Children," *The American Journal of Psychiatry*, February 2004.

Kemppainen, Liisa, MD, PhD, et al. "Predictors of Female Criminality: Findings From the Northern Finland 1966 Birth Cohort," The Journal of the American Academy of Child and Adolescent Psychiatry, July 2002.

McCrary, Gregg. A talk about how the Federal Bureau of Investigation identifies offenders at the 2002 annual meeting of the Canadian Psychiatric Association.

Meloy, J. Reid, PhD, et al. "Offender and Offense Characteristics of a Nonrandom Sample of Adolescent Mass Murderers," The Journal of the American Academy of Child and Adolescent Psychiatry, June 2001.

Paulson, Amanda. "Rebecca Sedgwick Suicide: What Response Is Needed to Combat Cyberbullying?" The Christian Science Monitor, October 15, 2013.

Shapiro, Ian. "Girl, 17, Pleads Guilty in Juvenile Court in Abuse of Autistic Boy in St. Mary's County," *The Washington Post,* May 29, 2014.

Sheidow, Ashli, PhD, et al. "The Relation of Antisocial Behavior Patterns and Changes in Internalizing Symptoms for a Sample of Inner-City Youth: Comorbidity within a Developmental Framework," *The Journal of Youth and Adolescence,* August 2008.

Simon, Robert, MD. Bad Men Do What Good Men Dream, American Psychiatric Publishing, 2008.

Smith, Abbe, JD. A commentary. "Six Adoptees Who Murdered -- Implications for Trial and Sentencing," *The Journal of the American Academy of Psychiatry and the Law,* October - December, 2001.

Steinberg, Annie, MD, et al. "Youth Hate Crime: Identification, Prevention, and Intervention," *The American Journal of Psychiatry,* May 2003.

Stone, Michael, MD. "Gradations of Antisociality and Responsivity to Psychosocial Therapies," *Psychotherapy for Personality Disorders,* edited by John Gunderson, MD, *et al,* American Psychiatric Press, 2000.

Stone, Michael, MD. "Serial Sexual Homicide," *The Journal of Personality Disorders,* February 2001.

Stout, David and Blumenthal, Mitchell. "Man Suspected in Anthrax Attacks Said to Commit Suicide," *The New York Times,* August 2, 2009.

Verhulst, Frank, MD. "The Fourteen-Year Prediction of Antisocial Behavior," *Developmental Psychopathy,* edited by James Hudziak, MD, American Psychiatric Publishing, 2006.

Welner, Michael, MD. One of the speakers at a symposium on "Defining Evil: Clinical and Forensic Implications," held at the 2002 annual meeting of the American Psychiatric Association.

Welner, Michael, MD. One of the speakers at a symposium on "How Psychiatry Defines Evil," held at the 2001 annual meeting of the American Psychiatric Association.

CHAPTER NINE

Arehart-Treichel, Joan. "Backing the Death Penalty: Expectations Versus Reality," *Psychiatric News*, July 19, 2002.

Arehart-Treichel, Joan. "Why So Many Americans Like the Death Penalty," *Psychiatric News*, July 19, 2002.

Michaud, Stephen and Hazelwood, Roy. *The Evil That Men Do*, St. Martin's Paperbacks, 1998.

Noguchi, Yasuki, and Iwasaka, Miho. "Hiding True Emotion: Micro-expressions," *Nature*, February 26, 2016.

Photos of Phillip and Nancy Garrido. The [Canadian] *Globe and Mail*, August 28, 2009.

Photos of some infamous evildoers. Cannon, Angie. "Crime Stories of the Century," U.S. News & World Report, December 6, 1999.

Photos of some infamous Evildoers. "Famously Evil," *U. S. News & World Report*, October 21, 2002.

Photos of Andy Williams. Published in www.Time.com, August 16, 2002 and in www.Time.com, August 19, 2002.

CHAPTER TEN

Anon. An interview with Adrian Raine, PhD, in *New Scientist*, May 2000.

Arehart-Treichel, Joan. An article about female stalkers, *Psychiatric News*, February 1, 2002.

Associated Press. "Accused BTK Killer 'Guy Next Door'," published by www.CBSNews.com on March 2, 2005.

Associated Press. "Pope Calls Sex Abuse by Priests a Crime," *The New York Times*, April 23, 2002.

Cannon, Angie. "Crime Stories of the Century," *U.S. News & World Report*, December 6, 1999.

Duenwald, Mary. "Who Would Abduct a Child? Previous Cases Offer Clues," *The New York Times*, August 27, 2002.

Ferranti, Jessica, MD, et al. "Characteristics of Female Homicide Offenders Found Not Guilty by Reason of Insanity," *The Journal of the American Academy of Psychiatry and the Law*, October-December 2013.

Gurian, Elizabeth. "Female Serial Murderers: Directions for Future Research on a Hidden Population," *International Journal of Offender Therapy and Comparative Criminology*, November 12, 2009.

Information about Federal Bureau of Investigation spy Robert Hansen, aired by CBS TV "60 Minutes" on December 16, 2001.

Information about Jarrod Ramos obtained from *The Annapolis Capital Gazette*, July 8, 2018.

Information about Jarrod Ramos obtained from *The Baltimore Sun*, July 2, 2018.

Information about Jarrod Ramos obtained from *The New York Times*, June 29, 2018.

Matejkowski, Jason, et al. "Characteristics of Persons with Severe Mental Illness Who Have Been Incarcerated for Murder," *The Journal of the American Academy of Psychiatry and the Law*, January-March 2008.

Reuters. "Harold Shipman English Physician Killed Hundreds," *The Washington Post*, January 14, 2004.

Rosengren, John. "When Loved Ones Steal," *The AARP Bulletin*, September 2018.

Simon, Robert, MD. *Bad Men Do What Good Men Dream*, American Psychiatric Publishing, 2008.

Sinclair, Leslie. "What Motivates Parents to Kill Their Child?" *Psychiatric News*, October 21, 2011.

Stone, Michael, MD. *The Anatomy of Evil*, Prometheus Books, 2009.

Stout, David. "Man Suspected in Anthrax Attacks Said to Commit Suicide," *The New York Times*, August 2, 2009.

Welner, Michael, MD. "The Only Safeguard Is Compassion," *The Newark Star-Ledger*, April 30, 2004.

Williams, Timothy. "Suspect Admits BTK Killings and Recounts Grisly Details," *The New York Times*, June 27, 2005.

Woodworth, Mike. "A Closer Look at Psychopathy," *The Dalhousie Psychiatry Monitor*, January 2004.

CHAPTER ELEVEN

Achenbach, Joel and Russakoff, Dale. "Portrait of a Teen at War," *The Washington Post*, April 29, 1999.

Arehart-Treichel, Joan. An article about some of the methods that the Federal Bureau of Investigation agents use to identify offenders, *Psychiatric News*, December 6, 2002.

Arehart-Treichel, Joan. An article about the psychological devastation that the Unabomber unleashed on his family, *Psychiatric News*, March 7, 2008.

Arehart-Treichel, Joan. An article about what makes sadists tick, *Psychiatric News*, July 5, 2002.

Arehart-Treichel, Joan. An interview with Robert Granacher, Jr, MD, in 2013 about what goes on in people's brains when they are lying.

Arehart-Treichel, Joan. "Intimate-Partner Murders Tied to Several Factors," *Psychiatric News*, August 1, 2003.

Arehart-Treichel, Joan. "Scientific Advances Changing Forensic Psychiatry," *Psychiatric News*, July 19, 2013.

Arehart-Treichel, Joan. "Understanding Roots of Hostility Could Divert Its Expression," *Psychiatric News*, March 7, 2003.

Arehart-Treichel, Joan. "Why Are We Taken In by Duplicity?" *Psychiatric News*, March 19, 2004.

Associated Press. "Accused BTK Killer 'Guy Next Door,'" published by www.CBS.com, March 2, 2005.

Barr, Cameron, et al. "Patient Admits Killing Psychiatrist, Police Say," *The Washington Post*, September 5, 2006.

Blair, James, PhD. A commentary. "Disregard for Others: Empathic Dysfunction or Emotional Volatility? The Relationship with Future Antisocial Behavior -- Reflections on Rhee et al (2013)," *Journal of Child Psychology and Psychiatry*, February 2013.

Bowley, Graham and Newman, Maria. "Gunman Is Described as Quiet and 'Always by Himself,'" *The New York Times*, April 17, 2007.

Cannon, Angie. "Crime Stories of the Century," *U.S. News & World Report*, December 6, 1999.

Duenwald, Mary. "Some Friends, Indeed, Do More Harm Than Good," *The New York Times*, September 10, 2002.

Eligon, John. "Wisconsin Suspect Killed Himself, Authorities Say," *The New York Times*, August 8, 2012.

Ford, Charles, MD. *Lies! Lies! Lies! -- the Psychology of Deceit*, American Psychiatric Press, 1996.

Friedman, Richard, MD. "Truth About Lies: Telling Them Can Reveal a Lot," *The New York Times*, July 29, 2003.

Goodstein, Laurie and Glaberson, William. The Well-Marked Roads to Homicidal Rage," *The New York Times*, April 19, 2007.

Hausman, Ken. "Does Pathological Lying Warrant Inclusion in DSM?" *Psychiatric News*, January 3, 2003.

Hirsch, Alan, MD. A workshop on the "Detection of Malingering" at the 2004 annual meeting of the American Psychiatric Association.

Hirsch, Alan, MD. "Practical Methods for Detecting Mendacity: A Case Study," The Journal of the American Academy of Psychiatry and the Law, October-December 2001.

Information about Antisocial Personality Disorder in The Diagnostic and Statistical Manual of Mental Disorders Fourth Edition Text Revision (DSM-IV-TR), published by the American Psychiatric Association in 2000.

Information about Schizoid Personality Disorder in The Diagnostic and Statistical Manual of Mental Disorders Fourth Edition Text Revision (DSM-IV-TR), published by the American Psychiatric Association in 2000.

James, David et al. "Abnormal Attentions Toward the British Royal Family: Factors Associated with Approach and Escalation," *The Journal of the American Academy of Psychiatry and the Law*, July - September 2010.

Jones, Tamara. "Muhammad's Ex-Wife Describes Death Threats," *The Washington Post*, November 19, 2003.

Kahn, Jennifer. "Can You Call a Nine-Year-Old a Psychopath?" *The New York Times*, May 11, 2012.

"Landru -- the Blue Beard of Gambai, France." A film aired by MHz TV on February 12, 2017.

Lock, Carrie. "Deception Detection," *Science News*, July 31, 2004.

Londono, Emesto. "Suspect Wasn't Violent, Father Says," *The Washington Post*, September 6, 2006.

Meloy, J. Reid, PhD, et al. "A Research Review of Public Figure Threats, Approaches, Attacks, and Assassinations in the United States," *The Journal of Forensic Sciences*, September 2004.

Meloy, J. Reid, PhD, et al. "Offender and Offense Characteristics of a Nonrandom Sample of Adolescent Mass Murderers," The Journal of the American Academy of Child and Adolescent Psychiatry, June 2001.

Merlino, Joseph, MD. Comments about some of the characteristics that might make people dangerous in the workplace, made at the 2002 annual meeting of the American Psychiatric Association.

Michaud, Stephen and Hazelwood, Roy. *The Evil That Men Do*, St. Martin's Paperbacks, 1998.

Moran, Mark. "Antisocial Personality Disorder: When Is It Treatable?" *Psychiatric News*, January 2, 2004.

Oliphant, Anne-Louise of the American College of Gastroenterology. "Stomach -- Not the Heart -- Offers Greater Lie Detection Accuracy," a press release published by www.Newswise.com on October 25, 2005.

Rosack, Jim. "Patient Charged with Murder of Schizophrenia Expert," *Psychiatric News*, October 6, 2006.

Schneider, Mary Beth and Walton, Richard. "Warrant Issued for Kansas Woman After 'Cruel Hoax," *The Indianapolis Star,* July 31, 2003.

Simon, Robert, MD. *Bad Men Do What Good Men Dream*, American Psychiatric Publishing, 2008.

Stone, Michael, MD. "Gradations of Antisociality and Responsivity to Psychosocial Therapies," *Psychotherapy for Personality Disorders*, edited by Gunderson, John et al, American Psychiatric Press, 2000.

Stone, Michael, MD. "Serial Sexual Homicide: Biological, Psychological," *The Journal of Personality Disorders*, February 2001.

Stone, Michael, MD. *The Anatomy of Evil*, Prometheus Books, 2009.

Streisand, Betsy and Cannon, Angie. "Betrayed by Their Silence?" *U.S. News & World Report*, March 19, 2001.

Streisand, Betsy and Cannon, Angie. "Exorcising the Pain," *U.S. News & World Report*, May 10, 1999.

Sullivan, Michale. "Gestures Reveal What the Lips Conceal," *Clinical Psychiatry News*, April 2002.

Waldinger, Robert. "Antisocial Personality Disorder," Psychiatry for Medical Students, American Psychiatric Press, 1997.

Welner, Michael, MD and Burgess, Ann, DN. Comments about characteristics indicating that someone might be sadistic, made at the 2002 annual meeting of the American Psychiatric Association.

Westen, Drew, PhD, et al. "Personality Diagnoses in Adolescence: DSM-IV II Diagnoses and an Empirically Derived Alternative," *The American Journal of Psychiatry*, May 2003.

CHAPTER TWELVE

Alvarez, Lizette. "Girl's Suicide Points to Rise in Apps Used by Cyberbullies," *The New York Times*, September 13, 2013.

Anon. "Father of Alleged School Shooter 'Scared for His Son,'" published by www.CNN.com ,March 16, 2001.

Anon. "That Was Not My Andy," published on www.ABCNews.com , September 6, 2001.

Arehart-Treichel, Joan. An article about relational bullying, *Psychiatric News*, July 6, 2007.

Arehart-Treichel, Joan. An article about school bullies, *Psychiatric News*, March 18, 2011.

Arehart-Treichel, Joan. "Childhood Bullying Correlates with Adult Domestic Violence," *Psychiatric News*, January 6, 2012.

Arehart-Treichel, Joan. "Understanding Roots of Hostility Could Divert Its Expression," *Psychiatric News*, March 7, 2003.

Arehart-Treichel, Joan. "Workplace Bullying Overlooked as Cause of Severe Stress," *Psychiatric News*, July 21, 2006.

Associated Press. "Fifty Years to Life for School Shooting," published by www.CBSNews.com , August 15, 2002.

Bender, Eve. "Bullying -- Not Victims -- Pose Greatest Violence Risk," *Psychiatric News*, May 18, 2003.

Bower, Bruce. "Violent Developments," *Science News*, May 27, 2006.

Carey, Benedict. "Fear in the Workplace: The Bullying Boss," *The New York Times*, June 22, 2004.

Copeland, William, PhD, et al. "Adult Psychiatric Outcomes of Bullying and Being Bullied by Peers in Childhood and Adolescence," *JAMA Psychiatry*, February 20, 2013.

Curry, Lynne, PhD. Beating the Workplace Bully: A Tactical Guide to Take Charge, the American Management Association, 2016.

Daly, Rich. "Latino Parents Avoid Talks About Sexual Orientation," *Psychiatric News*, December 7, 2007.

Falb, Kathryn, et al. "School Bullying Perpetration and Other Childhood Risk Factors as Predictors of Adult Intimate Partner Violence Perpetration," *Archives of Pediatrics and Adolescent Medicine*, October 2011.

Gadit, A. A. M., MD. "A Pilot Study of Bullying and Harassment Among Medical Professionals in Pakistan, Focusing on Psychiatry: Need for a Medical Ombudsman," *The Journal of Medical Ethics*, 2008.

Glew, Gwen, MD. "Bullying, Psychosocial Adjustment, and Academic Performance in Elementary School," Archives of Pediatrics & Adolescent Medicine, November 2005.

Herold, Eve. "Effects of Childhood Bullying Persist Far Into Midlife," a press release released by the American Psychiatric Association, April 16, 2014.

Hettena, Seth. "School Shooter Had 'Spilled Over,'" published on www. DailyNews.com , August 17, 2001.

Hinduja, Sameer, PhD, and Patchin, Justin. Bullying Beyond the School-yard, Corwin, 2015.

Information about "Cyberbullying: How to Spot the Warning Signs and Help Your Child Cope," published on www.Newswise.com , May 16, 2008.

Information about "Mean Girls, Bullies, Study Sheds Light on School Cliques," published on www.Newswise.com , March 7, 2008.

Lang, Susan. "Verbal Jabs and Stabs From Bullies Can Hurt and Even Kill," a press release released by Cornell University, August 29, 2002.

Lehmann, Christine. "Miss America Takes On Bullies and Their Victims," *Psychiatric News*, April 2, 2004.

Maier, James, MD. A letter regarding "APA Members Beat Back Bully-ing," published in *Psychiatric News*, March 19, 2004.

Medaris, Kim. "Study: Gifted Children Especially Vulnerable to Effects of Bullying," a press release released by Purdue University, April 6, 2006.

Nansel, Tonja, PhD, et al. "Relationships Between Bullying and Violence Among U.S. Youth," *Archives of Pediatrics and Adolescent Medicine*, April 2003.

Norton, Amy. "Sibling Bullying Can Lead to Depression, Anxiety in Victims," *MSN Healthy Living*, June 18, 2013.

Paulson, Amanda. "Rebecca Sedgwick Suicide: What Response Is Needed to Combat Cyberbullying?" *The Christian Science Monitor*, October 15, 2013.

Pope, Tara. "When the Bully Sits in the Next Cubicle," *The New York Times*, March 25, 2008.

Reaves, Jessica. "Charles 'Andy' Williams," published on www.Time.com , August 16, 2002.

Rosack, Jim. "AMA Warns of Mental Health Consequences of Bullying," *Psychiatric News*, August 12, 2002.

Staub, Ervin. *The Psychology of Good and* Evil, Cambridge University Press, 2003.

Twemlow, Stuart, MD, and Fonagy, Peter, PhD. "The Prevalence of Teachers Who Bully Students in Schools with Differing Levels of Behavioral Problems," *The American Journal of Psychiatry*, December 2005.

Watts, Vabren. "Effects of Childhood Bullying Extend Into Middle Age," *Psychiatric News*, May 12, 2014.

Xin, Dingding and Ce, Liu. "New Measures Introduced to Curb School Bullying," *China Daily U.S.A.*, November 15, 2016.

CHAPTER THIRTEEN

Arehart-Treichel, Joan. "Childhood Stalkers Not Kidding Around," *Psychiatric News*, June 19, 2009.

Arehart-Treichel, Joan. "Don't Underestimate Dangerousness of Female Stalkers, Study Urges," *Psychiatric News*, February 1, 2002.

Arehart-Treichel, Joan. "German Study Finds Stalking May Stop, But Victims' Suffering Does Not," *Psychiatric News*, September 2, 2005.

Dietz, Park, MD, and Martell, Daniel, PhD. "Commentary: Approaching and Stalking Public Figures -- A Prerequisite to Attack," *The Journal of the American Academy of Psychiatry and the Law*, July - September 2010.

Dressing, Harald, MD, et al. "Lifetime Prevalence and Impact of Stalking in a European Population," *The British Journal of Psychiatry*, August 2005.

James, David, DSc, et al. "Abnormal Attentions Toward the British Royal Family: Factors Associated with Approach and Escalation," *The Journal of the American Academy of Psychiatry and the Law*, July - September 2010.

James, David, DSc, et al. "Stalkers and Harassers of Royalty: The Role of Mental Illness and Motivation," *Psychological Medicine*, 2009.

James, David, DSc, et al. "The Role of Mental Disorder in Attacks on European Politicians 1990 - 2004, Acta Psychiatrica Scandinavica, 2007.

Lehmann, Christine. "Stalking Victims Endure Severe Psychological Stress," *Psychiatric News,* June 15, 2001.

Meloy, J. Reid, PhD, et al. "A Research Review of Public Figure Threats, Approaches, Attacks, and Assassinations in the United States," The Journal of Forensic Sciences, September 2004.

Moran, Mark. "Stalkers Inhabit a Reality All Their Own," *Psychiatric News,* November 5, 2004.

Proctor, Mike. Antidote for a Stalker, CreateSpace Independent Publishing Platform, 2013.

Purcell, Rosemary, PhD, et al. "Stalking Among Juveniles," *The British Journal of Psychiatry,* May 2009.

Stout, David and Blumenthal, Mitchell. "Man Suspected in Anthrax Attacks Said to Commit Suicide," *The New York Times,* August 2, 2008.

CHAPTER FOURTEEN

Anon. A report about Boy Scout leaders sexually abusing boys, aired on CBS TV News, April 23, 2019.

Anon. "Five Eyewitness News Talked Exclusively to Becker County Judge Who Granted Sex Offender Bail," aired on ABC TV "Five Eyewitness News," July 4, 2005.

Anon. "Target Throough a Rapist's Eyes -- Protect Yourself," posted on the Jeff Rense Program website, March 12, 2017.

Anon. "Ten Years After Polly, Another Predator Stalks Petaluma's Kids," posted on the SignOnSanDiego Forum website, October 14, 2003.

Arehart-Treichel, Joan. An article about exhibitionists, *Psychiatric News,* November 17, 2006.

Arehart-Treichel, Joan. An article about some of the methods Federal Bureau of Investigation agents use to identify offenders, *Psychiatric News,* December 6, 2002.

Arehart-Treichel, Joan. An interview with Gene Abel, MD, in January 2006.

Arehart-Treichel, Joan. An interview with Fred Berlin, MD, PhD., January 2006.

Arehart-Treichel, Joan. An interview with Saleh Fabian, MD, in January 2006.A

Arehart-Treichel, Joan. An interview with Igor Galynker, MD, PhD, in January 2006.

Arehart-Treichel, Joan. An interview with Linda Grassick, MD, in January 2006.

Arehart-Treichel, Joan. An interview with Richard Krueger, MD, in January 2006.

Arehart-Treichel, Joan. An interview with John Wojnowski on January 19, 2017.

Arehart-Treichel, Joan. An interview with Howard Zonana, MD, on November 30, 2005.

Arehart-Treichel, Joan. "Mood, Substance Abuse Disorders Common Among Sex Offenders," Psychiatric News, May 21, 2004.

Arehart-Treichel, Joan. "Pedophilia Often in Headlines, But Not in Research Labs," Psychiatric News, May 19, 2006.

Berryers, Colleen. "Potential Implications of Research on Genetic or Heritable Contributions to Pedophilia for the Objectivity of Criminal Law," Recent Advances in DNA Gene Sequencing, 2014.

Bower, Bruce. "Man of Prey," Science News, July 27, 2002.

Cohen, Lisa, PhD, and Galynker, Igor, MD, PhD. "Clinical Features of Pedophilia and Implications for Treatment," The Journal of Psychiatric Practice, September 2002.

Lamberg, Lynne. "Researchers Seek Roots of Pedophilia," The Journal of the American Medical Association, August 3, 2005.

MacMillan, Robert. "Sex Offender Lists Fall Short," The Washington Post, May 26, 2005.

Meijer, Joan. Date Rape: It's Not Your Fault, JEM Publishing, 2014.

Olson, Dave. "Sex Offender's Criminal History Started Early," The Free Republic, July 3, 2005.

Ramsland, Katherine. "Roy Hazelwood: Profiler of Sexual Crimes," The Crime Library, 2001.

Sax, Robin. Predators and Child Molesters: What Every Parent Needs to Know to Keep Kids Safe, Prometheus Books, 2009.

Simon, Robert, MD. *Bad Men Do What Good Men Dream*, American Psychiatric Publishing, 2008.

CHAPTER FIFTEEN

Anon. "Brady Book to Go on Sale," BBC News, December 4, 2001

Anon. Extensive evidence that a hostile, punitive parenting style is linked with an increased risk of developing antisocial behavior. Reported in the APA Research Agenda for DSM-V, June 17, 2002, p 170.

Anon. "Morderischer Abgang," *Der Spiegel*, 18/2002.

Anon. "Murderer's Tea Parties with Victim's Brother Stun England," www.Tabloid.net, August 10, 1998.

Anon. Sentencing of the Tarleys, CBS TV Evening News, April 19, 2019.

Arehart-Treichel, Joan. "Adult Criminality May Be Rooted in Troubling Childhood Behaviors," *Psychiatric News*, January 4, 2002.

Arehart-Treichel, Joan. "Aggression Comes in Four Types, Psychoanalyst Explains," *Psychiatric News*, April 4, 2008.

Arehart-Treichel, Joan. An article about bullying in affluent schools, *Psychiatric News*, March 18, 2011.

Arehart-Treichel, Joan. An article about why people act in a hostile manner, *Psychiatric News*, March 7, 2003.

Arehart-Treichel, Joan. An interview with David Olds, PhD, April 24, 2008.

Arehart-Treichel, Joan. An interview with Michael Stone, MD, March 20, 2008.

Arehart-Treichel, Joan. "Antisocial Behavior Contagious for Some Married Couples," *Psychiatric News*, February 7, 2003.

Arehart-Treichel, Joan. "Can Antisocial Behaviors Be Prevented?," *Psychiatric News*, August 1, 2008.

Arehart-Treichel, Joan. "Do Childhood Disorders Foretell Adult Psychopathology?," *Psychiatric News*, September 5, 2003.

Arehart-Treichel, Joan. "Early Disregard for Others' Pain May Predict Antisocial Behavior Later," *Psychiatric News*, March 15, 2013.

Arehart-Treichel, Joan. "Everyone Is in Danger of Committing Evil," *Psychiatric News*, June 15, 2001.

Arehart-Treichel, Joan. "Multiple Factors at Root of Antisocial Behavior," *Psychiatric News*, August 1, 2008.

Arehart-Treichel, Joan. "Program Empowers Parents to Deal with Conduct Disorder," *Psychiatric News*, January 5, 2007.

Arehart-Treichel, Joan. "Researchers Explore Link Between Animal Cruelty, Personality Disorders," *Psychiatric News*, September 20, 2002.

Arehart-Treichel, Joan. "Understanding Roots of Hostility Could Divert Its Expression," *Psychiatric News*, March 7, 2003.

Bender, Eve. "Expert Witness Describes Making of a Serial killer," *Psychiatric News*, December 3, 2004.

Bender, Eve. "'Special Chemistry' Forges Bond Between Killing Teams," *Psychiatric News*, December 3, 4004.

Carey, Benedict. "For the Worst of Us, the Diagnosis May Be Evil," *The New York Times*, February 8, 2005.

Cohen, Lisa, PhD, et al. "Heterosexual Male Perpetrators of Childhood Sexual Abuse: A Preliminary Neuropsychiatric Model, *Psychiatric Quarterly*, winter 2002.

Dines, Gail. "The Pornification of America," Newsmax, September 2016.

Ford, Charles, MD. *Lies! Lies! Lies! -- the Psychology of Deceit*, American Psychiatric Press, 1996.

Friedman, Richard, MD. "Beyond Anger: Studying the Subconscious Nature of Rage," *The New York Times*, November 12, 2002.

Gleyzer, Roman, MD, et al. "Animal Cruelty and Psychiatric Disorders," *The Journal of the American Academy of Psychiatry and the Law*, April-June, 2002.

Helgeland, Margareth, PhD, et al. "Continuities Between Emotional and Disruptive Behavior Disorders in Adolescence and Personality Disorders in Adulthood," *The American Journal of Psychiatry*, October 2005.

Information About Conduct Disorder in The Diagnostic and Statistical Manual of Mental Disorders Fourth Edition Text Revision (DSM-IV-TR), published by the American Psychiatric Association, 2000.

Kahn, Jennifer. "Can You Call a Nine-Year-Old a Psychopath?" *The New York Times*, May 11, 2012.

Keenan, Kate, PhD, and Wakschlag, Lauren, PhD. "Are Oppositional Defiant and Conduct Disorder Symptoms Normative Behaviors in Preschoolers? A Comparison of Referred and Nonreferred Children," *The American Journal of Psychiatry*, February 2004.

Kim-Cohen, Julia, PhD, et al. "Prior Juvenile Diagnoses in Adults with Mental Disorder," *The Archives of General Psychiatry*, July 2003.

Marquardt, Tom. "I Think My Parents Are Dead," *The Washingtonian*, January 1986.

McLeod, Saul. Information about the Milgram shock experiment, published on www.simplypsychology.org/milgram.html, 2017.

Meloy, J. Reid, PhD, et al. "Offender and Offense Characteristics of a Nonrandom Sample of Adolescent Mass Murderers," *The Journal of the American Academy of Child and Adolescent Psychiatry*, June 2001.

Michaud, Stephen and Hazelwood, Roy. *The Evil That Men Do*, St. Martin's Paperbacks, 1998.

Moran, Mark. "Psychiatrists Lament Decline of Key Treatment Modality," *Psychiatric News*, July 3, 2009.

Nelken, Michael, MD. Comments about the "Step into Evil" at the 2001 annual meeting of the American Academy of Psychoanalysis.

Paris, Joel, MD. Nature and Nurture in Psychiatry, American Psychiatric Press, 1999.

Ramsland, Katherine. "Roy Hazelwood: Profiler of Sexual Crimes," The Crime Library, 2001.

Satterfield, J. H. and Schell, A. "A Prospective Study of Hyperactive Boys with Conduct Problems and Normal Boys: Adolescent and Adult Criminality," *The Journal of the American Academy of Child and Adolescent Psychiatry*, December 1997.

Sederer, Lloyd, MD. "Evil -- Marvelously Portrayed -- Why Do You Watch 'House of Cards'?" *The Huffington Post*, March 4, 2014.

Simonoff, Emily, MD. "Predictors of Antisocial Personality," The British Journal of Psychiatry, February 2004.

Staub, Ervin, PhD. *The Psychology of Good and Evil*, Cambridge University Press, 2003.

Stevenson, Jim, and Goodman, Robert. "The Association Between Behavior at Age Three Years and Adult Criminality," *The British Journal of Psychiatry*, September 2001.

Stone, Michael, MD. Comments made at a sadistic personality symposium at the 2002 annual meeting of the American Psychiatric Association.

Stone, Michael, MD. Comments made at the "Personality and Evil: Psychiatric Understanding" symposium at the 2001 annual meeting of the American Psychiatric Association.

Stone, Michael, MD. *The Anatomy of Evil*, Prometheus Books, 2009.

Verhulst, Frank, MD. "The Fourteen-Year Prediction of Antisocial Behavior," Developmental Psychopathology and Wellness, edited by James Hudziak, MD, American Psychiatric Publishing, 2008.

Welner, Michael, MD. Comments made at a sadistic personality symposium at the 2002 annual meeting of the American Psychiatric Association.

Williams, Timothy. "Suspect Admits B.T.K. Killings and Recounts Grisly Details," *The New York Times*, June 27, 2005.

Zimbardo, Philip, PhD. "Transforming People Into Perpetrators of Evil," a lecture given at the Holocaust Studies Center, Sonoma State University, March 9, 1999.

AUTHOR BIOGRAPHY

Joan Arehart-Treichel is an award-winning science writer who, over the years, was on the staff of *Science News Magazine*; has written articles about scientific advances for *New York Magazine, Glamour, Harper's Bazaar, Psychology Today, Sexology, The Washington Post,* and other consumer publications; and has written four previous books about scientific advances for the public, notably *Biotypes: The Critical Link Between Your Personality and Your Health,* which was published by Times Books (*The New York Times* book publishing company) and sold in the United States, Canada, England, and France.

For 15 years, she worked as a senior staff writer for *Psychiatric News*, a newspaper published by the American Psychiatric Association for psychiatrists throughout the United States. During this period, she covered research advances in various domains of psychiatry, including forensic psychiatry. And during her coverage of forensic psychiatry, she came to know a number of leading authorities on evildoers. She also had face-to-face contact with some individuals who had committed grisly deeds -- say, a young woman in the forensic wing of a mental hospital who had killed her parents and a death-row prisoner at San Quentin State Prison in California.

Her book is thus based on what she has learned about evildoers during this time period—information that she believes is not just provocative, or frightening, but that could help people shield themselves from such individuals.

CPSIA information can be obtained
at www.ICGtesting.com
Printed in the USA
BVHW071012171222
654331BV00011B/754